FIRENZE
MVSEI

PITTI PALACE
Palatine Gallery

Alessandro Cecchi
Maddalena De Luca Savelli

sillabe

ISBN 978-88-8347-554-2
© 2010 Ministero per i Beni e le Attività Culturali
Soprintendenza Speciale per il Patrimonio Storico, Artistico
ed Etnoantropologico e per il Polo Museale della città di Firenze

A publication by
s i l l a b e s.r.l.
Livorno
www.sillabe.it

Managing editor: *Maddalena Paola Winspeare*
Graphic design and cover lay-out: *Laura Belforte*
English editing: *Giulia Bastianelli*
Diagrams of the rooms: *Saimon Toncelli*
Translation: *Catherine Burnett*

Printing: *Media Print, Livorno*

Photo Credits: *Archivio sillabe/Foto Paolo Nannoni, Cristian Ceccanti;
Archivio fotografico della Soprintendenza SPSAE e per il Polo Museale
della città di Firenze*

FIRENZE
MVSEI   Firenze Musei is a registered trademark of Sergio Bianco

Reprint	Year
0 1 2 3 4 5 6 7 8 9 10	2010 2011 2012 2013 2014 2015 2016 2017 2018 2019 2020

CONTENTS

Thanks to this comprehensive and easy-to-read official guidebook, conceived and overseen by the director Alessandro Cecchi and Maddalena De Luca Savelli, the Palatine Gallery has now become a little more accessible to its visitors. In particular to those who, aside from enjoying the experience of the visit in terms of the magnificence, richness and variety of the rooms and collections, wish to obtain a basic, on-the-spot point of reference and come away with a publication which can serve both as a memento and a stimulus for further study.

The Palatine Gallery is a sublime embodiment of the role Palazzo Pitti held for centuries as a dynastic palace; it is full of works of art collected by the Medici and Lorraine families, and it is one of the most "difficult" museums for the general public. The baroque magnificence of the furnishings and the captivating Baroque-to-Romantic wall paintings alone demand attention and excite admiration, but as the main attraction of the museum lies in the masterpieces by great and glorious artists such as Botticelli, Andrea del Sarto, Raphael, Titian and Rubens to name but a few of the most well-known, visitors can become confused and tired and perhaps lose their bearings as they explore the walls, which are literally covered in two or even three rows of paintings, trying to find the works they want to see.

This guidebook amiably and discretely addresses these considerations, which are ingrained in the architecture and the "a quadreria" style of mounting (with paintings covering the walls according to decorative and not historical criteria). It does not simplify a complex experience, but it leads visitors along a well thought-out path and provides a grounded anthology of the outstanding works and furnishings on display. Thanks to the maps, diagrams, photographs, clear numbering, intuitive cross-referencing and clear, incisive information, reading a page and understanding – where we are, what we are looking at, the history – becomes instantly apparent, with our aesthetic sensibilities gratified as well as our sense of reason.

With this guide, Firenze Musei and the publisher Sillabe truly offer visitors an exemplary "accompaniment" to the visit which, I am sure, will help preserve the recollection of the hours passed in this treasure chest of art and memories.

Cristina Acidini
Soprintendente per il Patrimonio Storico,
Artistico ed Etnoantropologico
e per il Polo Museale della città di Firenze

Pietro da Cortona, fresco,
Mars Room (detail)

The Palatine Gallery

The Palatine Gallery opened to the public in 1834 under Leopold II, the last of the Hapsburg-Lorraine Grand Dukes. It is situated in the sumptuous rooms on the main floor of Palazzo Pitti in the Winter Apartments and the state rooms of the Medici dynasty Grand Dukes. Its rooms still retain the appearance and character they had when they were inhabited in centuries past, as shown by the rich cycles of seventeenth to nineteenth-century frescoes and the furnishings, including the invaluable sixteenth to nineteenth-century semi-precious stone and scagliola tables. Given that it is royal palace with generations of sovereigns as inhabitants, the history of the Palatine Gallery is indissolubly linked to its surroundings as well as its ruling families: the Medicis, who controlled the destiny of the Tuscan state for two centuries from 1537 to 1737, and the Lorraines, Grand Dukes up to 1859 with a brief interlude of French occupation. The Gallery's collections are the result of Medici and Lorraine collecting, more so than in any other state museum in Florence, and from the seventeenth century onwards the works have been part of the Palace's furnishings.

Eleanor of Toledo, the Spanish consort of Duke Cosimo I, bought the Palace from the Pitti family in 1549 and during the second half of the century grandiose extensions were carried out with one of the most impressive and monumental results being the creation of the Ammannati Courtyard. Cosimo, then later his sons Francesco and Ferdinando I, commissioned this building work including interior renovations in order to prepare the palace to receive the Grand Ducal family and the Court before they moved in at the end of the century (following a long period of residence in Palazzo Vecchio). Grand Dukes Cosimo II and then Ferdinando II oversaw the completion of the renovations in the seventeenth century, bringing the Palace and its façade to their current state with the exception of the two 'rondeaux' (perpendicular wings) built by the Lorraine family in the eighteenth and nineteenth centuries.

In particular, Ferdinando II de' Medici's marriage in 1634 to Vittoria delle Rovere, the last member of the dynasty of the Dukes of Urbino, marked the beginning of the extensive renovations in the Palace and the Boboli Gardens. Renowned artists created a great number of works of art throughout the Summer Apartment (now the Silver Museum), with its Salon frescoed by Giovanni da San Giovanni and his successors, and the Winter Apartment on the first floor with the State Rooms of the Planets frescoed by Pietro da Cortona and his assistants during the first half of the seventeenth century. At the same time, the Grand Dukes and their brothers continued to enrich the collections which, shortly afterwards in 1711, would be joined by Vittoria della Rovere's masterpieces (now divided between the Palatine Gallery and the Uffizi Gallery).

One of the most prominent figures was the Prince then Cardinal Leopoldo de' Medici, Ferdinando's brother and a resident in the Palace. He was a

Venus Room

keen collector especially of Venetian painting, and he was also responsible for the beginnings of the drawing and self-portrait collections at the Uffizi. The last Medicis were a match for their predecessors and Grand Prince Ferdinando, Grand Duke Cosimo III's son who died before his father in 1713, contributed in a determining manner to the acquisition of masterpieces from Florentine and Tuscan churches. The works in the Grand Prince's collections, like those in all Italian galleries in the baroque era, were exhibited 'a quadreria' (according to decorative and not historical criteria); they covered the walls of his living quarters in the Royal Apartments, encased like dazzling gems in their settings in rich carved and gilded frames.

An important chapter in the palace's collecting history was written by Ferdinand III and Leopold II. They were the most active rulers of the Lorraine dynasty in terms of the enrichment of the Medici collections they had inherited, bound by the famous 'Family Pact' stipulated by the Electress Palatine Anna Maria Luisa de' Medici; the Electress Palatine was the last of her dynasty, which died out in the male line when her brother Gian Gastone died in 1737.

Every painting in the Palatine Gallery is like a single tile in a magnificent mosaic completed over the course of the centuries thanks to the enlightened and enthusiastic collectors of the two dynasties. It is for this reason that the captions and profiles which accompany each work carry an initial identifying the meritorious buyer of the work. Furthermore, given that the current display mounted by the Lorraines follows the seventeenth-century layout from the time of Grand Prince Ferdinando and can cause visitors to become disorientated and confused due to the many rows of paintings above one another, this guide has been given a different structure compared to traditional handbooks. It has topographic diagrams of the walls which allow visitors to clearly see and identify the most significant works, marked out by a colour image and a short profile instead of the concise captions found in other manuals.

These are the most important new developments in this guidebook, which is dedicated solely to the paintings on display in the Palatine Gallery and which takes the place of still valid version, in terms of historic information, written by Marco Chiarini. All that remains for the authors to do is to wish people an enjoyable visit to this "princely" collection, which has maintained its fascination intact over the centuries and now holds 815 paintings (922 including those in the Royal Apartments), including groups of the most important works of art in the world by Raphael and Andrea del Sarto, masterpieces by Pontormo, Bronzino, Giorgione, Titian, Rubens and other great masters of Italian and foreign schools from the fifteenth to eighteenth centuries.

Alessandro Cecchi
Director of the Palatine Gallery
and Royal Apartments
and the Boboli Gardens

Prometheus Room

Reading Guide

The walls of the rooms are numbered from I to IV in a clockwise direction beginning at the entrance, and they are depicted with a numbered reference diagram; the particularly noteworthy works are identified with a small picture.

The featured artists and collectors of the Medici or Hapsburg Lorraine families (denoted with an initial at the bottom of the profiles) are listed at the end of the book.

This guide contains information only about the Palatine Gallery and not the Royal Apartments, although the Apartments are part of the current museum visit.

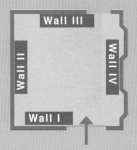

Footmen's Antechamber
(Anticamera degli Staffieri)

This room was originally at the southern end of the sixteenth century loggia on the piano nobile (main floor) of the palace. It was open to the courtyard and gave access to the Grand Duke's apartment. As you enter the room there are two niches in richly-veined Seravezza marble which used to be open, although now bronze grating closes the way through to the vestibule. Over the centuries these niches have held many different statues. Currently there are two *Fauns with Panthers*, Roman copies from a late-Hellenistic original.

The pictorial decorations can be dated to 1790 and were done by Giuseppe Maria Terreni, an artist appointed at the time by Grand Duke Peter Leopold of Hapsburg Lorraine to work in Palazzo Pitti.

A portrait of *Grand Prince Ferdinando de' Medici* by Anton Domenico Gabbiani (inv. 1890 no. 2731, *c.* 1683) hangs on the right-hand wall; the Grand Prince was Cosimo III's son, a great patron of the arts as well as a collector and musicologist. A portrait of the Prince's brother *Grand Duke Gian Gastone de' Medici* by Franz Ferdinand Richter hangs on the left-hand wall (inv. 1890 no. 3805); Gian Gastone was the last Grand Duke of the Medici dynasty and is depicted with the emblems of power (the sceptre and crown) and the Cross of the Order of St. Stephen.

As mentioned above, the two niches towards the entrance hold two marble sculptures of a *Faun with a Panther* which are sixteenth-century copies of a Roman work of art from the Imperial era (inv. OdA nos. 634–635). They were bought in 1584 by Cardinal Ferdinando de' Medici from the Capranica Della Valle collection in Roma and placed in the Villa Medici.

They were transferred to Palazzo Pitti in Florence between 1787 and 1788.

The two console tables hold a marble bust by Giuseppe Belli of *Ferdinand II of Hapsburg Lorraine*, named Grand Duke of Tuscany in 1791 (inv. OdA no. 674), and a bronze bust by the sculptor Baccio Bandinelli of *Cosimo I de' Medici* (inv. OdA no. 671), which is an official likeness of Cosimo I and has been at Palazzo Pitti since its completion.

Two full-length sculptures stand on either side of the entrance to the Statue Gallery: the *Mercury* by Pietro Francavilla, formerly in the Boboli Gardens before the end of the seventeenth century and restored in 1775 by Innocenzo Spinazzi (1604, inv. OdA no. 659), and the *Bacchus* by Baccio Bandinelli which was originally conceived as an *Adam* for Florence Cathedral, commissioned in 1549 by Cosimo I, who had it placed first in Palazzo Vecchio then in Palazzo Pitti (inv. OdA no. 658).

11

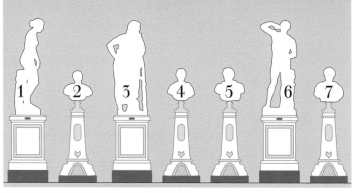

I-1
Roman art,
1st–2nd century AD
Aphrodite of Cnidus
marble, inv. OdA 1911
no. 670
doc. at Palazzo Pitti in 1568
F I. M (1588)
This work is based on the famous statue by Praxiteles (c. 360 BC) sculpted for the city of Cnidus, where it was placed in an open setting so it could be admired from all sides.

I-2
Florentine school,
17th century (?)
Portrait of the so-called Virginio
marble, inv. OdA 1911
no. 687

I-3
Roman art,
2nd century AD
Aesculapius
marble, inv. OdA 1911
no. 669
doc. in 1711–1712; doc. at Palazzo Pitti c. 1794
C III. M
In the 17th century this statue was thought to be of a philosopher, although in actual fact it portrays Aesculapius, the Greek god (Asclepius) of medicine with his customary

Statue Gallery (Galleria delle Statue)

This Gallery forms the mid-section of the vast open loggia which looked over the Ammannati Courtyard. In 1620 Cosimo II used it as a picture gallery and a display area for precious furnishings. During the first Lorraine era (1737–1799) the loggia was closed off and used as a "Guards' Room" (Sala delle Guardie). In 1790 the room was put to a more fitting use when it was decorated by Giuseppe Maria Terreni and transformed into the current Statue Gallery. The room was filled with statues and busts from Cardinal Ferdinando's former collection from the Villa Medici in Rome. In the 19th century the statues were joined by fourteen busts which were put on display in the adjacent Room of the Niches.

Along with the busts of ancient emperors, the room also holds busts of the Grand Dukes of Tuscany: the *Portrait of Peter Leopold* from 1773 above the entrance by Innocenzo Spinazzi (inv. OdA 1911 no. 673), and the *Portrait of Cosimo II* (Florentine school, 18th century) above the middle door on the left hand wall (inv. OdA 1911 no. 672). This portrait of Cosimo II, along with another bust of Cosimo I now not in situ, represented the Medici dynasty alongside the Lorraine dynasty.

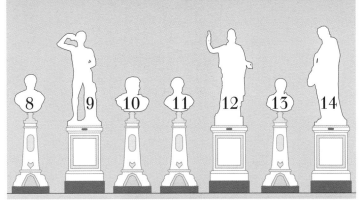

attribute of the snake-entwined staff.

I-4
Roman art,
2nd century AD
(Antonine era)
Portrait of a Woman
marble, inv. OdA 1911
no. 679
c. 170 AD

I-5
Roman art,
2nd century AD (late
Antonine era)
Portrait of Lucius Verus
marble, inv. OdA 1911
no. 683
160–169 AD
F I. M (1588)

I-6
Roman art,
2nd century AD
Athlete
marble, inv. OdA 1911
no. 668
doc. at Palazzo Pitti 1584
F I. M (1588)

This portrayal of an athlete pouring oil into his left hand gave rise to the term 'the Pitti type' used to describe copies of the statue. The Polycletian-School original dates back to 380 BC. When this work was in the Gallery of the Villa Medici in Rome, it was positioned in front of the other *Athlete* now on display here in Palazzo Pitti (I-9).

I-1

13

I-5   I-6

I-7
Roman art,
2nd century AD
(Antonine era)
Portrait of Antoninus Pius
marble, inv. OdA 1911
no. 684
F I. M

I-8
Roman art,
2nd century AD
Portrait of Marcus Aurelius
marble, inv. OdA 1911
no. 685
160–180 AD
F I. M (1588)

I-9
Roman art,
2nd century AD
Athlete
marble, inv. OdA 1911
no. 667
doc. at Palazzo Pitti 1584
F I. M (1588)
This sculpture is based on an original from 350–330 BC, although the head and part of the arms and legs were redone in the 18th century. The work has similar characteristics to the series of works identified as 'the Munich type', in reference to the *Athlete* on display in the German city. When this sculpture was in the Gallery of the Villa Medici in Rome, it was positioned in front of

the other *Athlete* now on display here in Palazzo Pitti (I-6).

I-10
Florentine school,
16th–17th century
Portrait of Caracalla
marble, inv. OdA 1911
no. 678

I-11
Roman art,
2nd century AD
Portrait of a Man
marble, inv. OdA 1911
no. 675
130–140 AD

I-9

I-14

I-12
Roman art,
2nd century AD
Athena (Justinian type)
marble, inv. OdA 1911
no. 666
F I. M (1588)

I-13
Roman art
*Portrait known as
'of Ovid'*
marble, inv. Od A 1911
no. 686

I-14
Roman art,
2nd century AD
Hygieia
marble, inv. OdA 1911
no. 665
100–150 AD
F I. M; C III. M
doc. in 1715; doc. at
Palazzo Pitti *post* 1788
Aesculapius' daughter
Hygieia was venerated as
the goddess of health. This
statue was bought in Rome
by Cardinal Ferdinando
de' Medici and is based on
a Hellenistic original.

II-1
Roman art,
2nd century AD
(Antonine era)
Mercury
marble, inv. OdA 1911
no. 664
F I. M

II-2
Florentine school,
17th century
*Portrait of an
Unknown Man*
marble, inv. OdA 1911
no. 657

II-3
Roman art,
2nd century AD
*Portrait of Marcus
Aurelius as a Young
Man*
marble, inv. OdA 1911
no. 682
144–147 AD

II-4
Roman art,
2nd century AD
Satyr and Pan
marble, inv. OdA 1911
no. 663
c. 150 AD
F I. M (1588)

This is a Roman version of
the *Resting Satyr* by Praxiteles (*c.* 350 BC). The group
comes from the Villa Medici in Rome, like the other

Satyr and Pan statue now
in Palazzo Pitti (II-7).

II-5
Roman art,
2nd century AD (?)
Portrait of a Man
marble, inv. OdA 1911
no. 656
130–140 AD

II-6
Roman art,
2nd century AD
(Antonine era)
*Portrait of Antoninus
Pius*
marble, inv. OdA 1911
no. 681
138–161 AD
F I. M (1588)

II-7
Roman art,
2nd century AD
Satyr and Pan
marble, inv. OdA 1911
no. 662
F I. M (1588)

The satyr is a goat-like
mythological creature,
portrayed here with Pan, a
rural god of shepherds and
herds. This is a Roman version from around 150 AD of
the *Resting Satyr* by Praxiteles (*c.* 350 BC). The work
came from the Villa Medici
in Rome, where it was dis-
played along with another
Satyr and Pan statue now
in Palazzo Pitti (II-4).

II-4

16

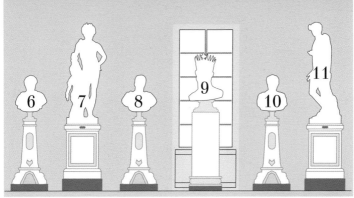

II-8
Roman art, early
Imperial Era
Head of a Doryphoros
marble, inv. OdA 1911
no. 688
F I. M

This head of a 'Doryphoros', a Spear-Bearer, is a copy of the famous original by Polycletus which established the rules of measurement to be used when sculpting. This is a modern bust, probably from the 16th century.

II-9
Giovan Battista
Ferrucci del Tadda
and Baccio Bandinelli's
studio
Portrait of Grand Duke Cosimo I
bronze, inv. OdA 1911
no. 604
1587
Fr I. M

This colossal bronze bust was commissioned by Francesco I in homage to his father. It was originally intended for the courtyard of Palazzo Pitti above an epitaph, although it was placed in the Room of the Niches in 1590. It was moved several times to various locations inside the Palace, before only recently being positioned in the Statue Gallery.

II-10
Roman art
Portrait of Septimius Severus
marble, inv. OdA 1911
no. 676
F I. M (1588)

II-11
Roman art,
1st century AD (?)
Mercury
marble, inv. OdA 1911
no. 661
F I. M (1588)

II-8

II-9

17

Castagnoli Room (Sala del Castagnoli)

In the seventeenth century this area actually accommodated two rooms in the Grand Duchess' apartment; one was used as her bedroom and the other as a utility room for her chambermaids. Between 1810 and 1812, during French rule, the two rooms were joined together as part of a renovation project planned by the architect Giuseppe Cacialli to form a communal Antechamber for the Emperor and Empress' new apartments. Giuseppe Castagnoli carried out the pictorial decorations on the walls and the ceiling in 1812 with *Apollo driving the Chariot of the Sun*. When the Lorraines returned some busts were added to the room with effigies of *Grand Duke Peter Leopold of Lorraine with allegories of Prudence and Plenty*, *Grand Duke Ferdinand II of Lorraine with allegories of Fortitude and Peace* and *Portraits of the Medicis and Hapsburg Lorraines*, emphasising the continuity between the two dynasties.

The two monumental full-length marble sculptures on display in this room were bought in 1584 by Cardinal Ferdinando de' Medici from the Capranica Della Valle collection in Rome and placed in the Villa Medici before being transferred to Palazzo Pitti in Florence in 1785.

Roman art from the Trajan era
Barbarian Prisoner
marble, inv. OdA no. 440
Fl. M (1584)

Roman art from the 2nd century AD
Caesar Augustus
marble, inv. OdA no. 439
Fl. M

Galleria dei Lavori
(Workshop) of the
Opificio delle Pietre
Dure from a design by
Giovan Battista Giorgi,
base by Giovanni
Dupré
Table known as the
Table of the Muses
commesso in semi-precious stones and bronze,
inv. OdA no. 1526
1853

19

Allegories Room (Sala delle Allegorie)

This room was Grand Duchess Vittoria della Rovere's bedchamber and it is the only room in this wing of the Palace, known as the "Volterrano Wing" (Quartiere del Volterrano), to still have its original stuccoed and frescoed ceiling. This decorative work was done around 1658 by Baldassarre Franceschini, known as Il Volterrano, inspired by the works designed by Pietro da Cortona for the Rooms of the Planets, and perhaps carried out by the same Roman assistants. The allegories on the ceiling allude to the name and the virtue of the Grand Duchess with Fame, Fortitude and Victory in the centre, and Modesty, Peace, Truth and Wisdom in the side sections.

In the centre of the room

Emilio Zocchi
Young Michelangelo sculpting a Faun
marble, inv. OdA no. 453
c. 1682
signed

Wall I

I-1
Carracci family circle
Portrait of a Man
paper affixed to canvas,
inv. 1912 no. 310
c. 1587–1588
doc. at Palazzo Pitti in 1834

I-2
Benedetto Luti
Head of a Young Girl
pastel on paper, inv. 1890
no. 819
GPF. M

I-3
Benedetto Luti
Head of a Cherub
pastel on paper, inv. 1890
no. 821
GPF. M

I-4
Bolognese school,
17th century (Mastelletta?)
Rest on the Flight into Egypt
wood panel, inv. 1912
no. 350
doc. at Palazzo Pitti in 1834

I-9

I-10

I-11

I-5

Carlo Antonio Sacconi
Portrait of an Oriental
canvas, inv. 1890 no. 2370
c. 1698
doc. at Palazzo Pitti in
1828
GPF. M (1713)

I-6

Justus Suttermans
Portrait of a Man in Armour
canvas, inv. 1890 no. 769
c. 1645–1650
doc. in 1704; doc. at
Palazzo Pitti in 1828

I-7

Justus Suttermans
Portrait of Caterina Puliciani
canvas, inv. 1890 no. 1071
c. 1650–1660
doc. in 1704

I-8

Volterrano
Venal Love
fresco on slate, inv. 1912
no. 105
c. 1642
doc. at Palazzo Pitti in
1828
GPF. M (1713)

I-9

Livio Mehus
The Genius of Sculpture
canvas , inv. 1890 no. 5337
GPF. M

This painting was done
around 1650 at the same
time as its counterpart, *The
Genius of Painting*, now at
the Prado Museum, and
was probably bought by
Grand Prince Ferdinando
de' Medici in 1691 when
the artist died. It depicts a
young man, perhaps an artist or a connoisseur, holding a tablet inscribed with
the word "Genio" ("Gen-
ius") and pointing out two
famous ancient sculptures:
a *Minerva* in gilded bronze
after a Hellenistic original,

and the lower part of the
famous *Farnese Hercules*.

I-10

Justus Suttermans
*The Florentine Senate
swearing Loyalty
to Ferdinando II
de' Medici*
canvas, inv. 1890, no. 9692
c. 1624

This work was done around
1624 and is a small-scale
preparatory design for a
large painting originally
intended for the Room of
the Niches in Palazzo Pitti,
now in the Niobe Room in
the Uffizi Gallery. It was
painted for the Florentine
Senate's swearing of loy-
alty ceremony for the young
Ferdinando, orphaned in
1621 by his father Cosimo II
and at that point still under the guardianship of the
Regents, his mother Maria
Magdalena of Austria and

his grandmother Christine
of Lorraine.

I-11

Volterrano
*The Trick of the Parish
Priest Arlotto*
canvas, inv. 1890 no. 582
1640
GC. M; GPF. M

This painting is perhaps the
artist's most well known
work inspired by the stories
of the tricks of the parish
priest Arlotto, a popular
character in fifteenth-cen-
tury Florence. The painting
can be dated to 1640 and is
documented as belonging
to a Florentine man, Francesco Parrocchiani, before
it joined the collections
of Cardinal Giovan Carlo
de' Medici, who commis-
sioned another two scenes.
When the Cardinal died
the painting passed into
Grand Prince Ferdinando's
collection.

21

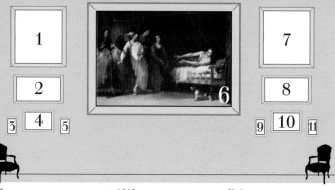

I-12
Justus Suttermans
Portrait of Cosimo III de' Medici
canvas, inv. 1890 no. 2875
c. 1665

I-13
Justus Suttermans
Portrait of Signor Puliciani
canvas, inv. 1890 no. 1059
c. 1650–1660
doc. in 1704

I-14
Volterrano
Sleeping Cupid
fresco on slate, inv. 1912 no. 105

c. 1642
doc. at Palazzo Pitti in 1828
GPF. M (1713)

Wall II

II-1
Artemisia Gentileschi
Madonna and Child
canvas, inv. 1890 no. 2129
c. 1610–1611
doc. at Palazzo Pitti in 1663

II-2
Vasari's school
Birth of the Virgin
wood panel, inv. 1890 no. 8684
1568
doc. at Palazzo Pitti in 1928

II-3
Anastagio Fontebuoni (?)
Young St. John in the Desert
copper, inv. 1890 no. 1465
early 17th century
doc. in 1777

II-4
Florentine school, 17th century
Infant Jesus Asleep on the Cross
wood panel, inv. 1890 no. 1358

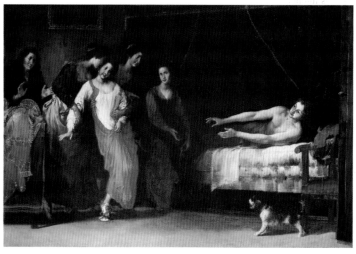

II-

II-5
Cristofano Allori
Madonna and Child
copper, inv. 1890 no. 1498
1620
signed: CRISTOFANO
ALLORI D:O IL BRONZINO
GPF. M

II-6
Giovanni da San
Giovanni
First Night of Marriage
canvas, inv. 1890 no. 2120
DL. M

This painting was done
in 1620–1622, for Don
Lorenzo de' Medici, Grand
Duke Cosimo II's brother,
and was intended for the
Villa di Castello. It depicts
a young bashful bride ac-
companied by some women
to her marriage bed, where
her eager husband is waiting for her with open arms.
The room where the scene
is set is particularly inter-
esting as it is richly decorated and painted with a
wealth of details in what
may be a unique case in
seventeenth-century Ital-
ian painting.

II-7
Gregorio Pagani
*Tobias restoring the
Sight of his Father*
canvas, inv. 1890 no. 1559
signed and dated 1604
doc. in 1605; doc. at
Palazzo Pitti in 1928

II-8
Vasari's school
Vision of Count Ugo
wood panel, inv. 1890
no. 8685
1568
doc. at Palazzo Pitti in
1928

II-9
Girolamo Macchietti
Venus and Adonis
wood panel, inv. 1890
no. 6266
c. 1570–1572
doc. in 1704

II-10
Cristofano Allori
copy of the *St. Mary
Magdalene Reading* by
Correggio
copper, inv. 1890 no. 1344
doc. at Palazzo Pitti in
1666

II-11
Maso da San Friano
*Portrait of Elena Gaddi
Quaratesi*
wood panel, inv. 1890
no. 1552
signed: ... Tommaso da
S.Frian...
doc. in 1780

III-1
Alessandro Allori
*Portrait of a Medici
Noblewoman*
wood panel, inv. Poggio
Imperiale no. 548
c. 1570–1572
doc. at Palazzo Pitti in
1828

III-2
Cristofano
dell'Altissimo
*Portrait of Clarice
Ridolfi Altoviti*
wood panel, inv. 1912
no. 327
doc. in 1599

III-3
Justus Suttermans
*Portrait of Archduke
Charles of Austria*
canvas, inv. 1912 no. 293
1623–1625
L. M (1675)

III-4
Volterrano
*Portrait of Antonio
Baldinucci*
pastel on paper, inv. 1890
no. 2578
ante 1681
signed: ... fatto da Baldas-
sar Franceschini detto il
Volterrano...
doc. at Palazzo Pitti in
1775

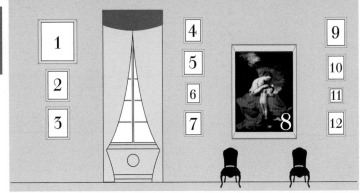

III-5
Cigoli
St. Mary Magdalene Penitent
canvas, inv. 1890 no. 2173
signed and dated 1605
doc. at Palazzo Pitti in 1928
C. M (1666)

III-6
Giovanni da San Giovanni
Mystical Marriage of St. Catherine of Alexandria
canvas, inv. 1890 no. 1565
1634
DL. M (1649)

III-7
Alessandro Allori
Portrait of a Woman
wood panel, inv. 1912 no. 204
doc. at Palazzo Pitti in 1828

III-8
Cristofano dell'Altissimo
Portrait of Isabella Ruini (?)
wood panel, inv. 1912 no. 315
doc. at Palazzo Pitti in 1828

III-9
Justus Suttermans
Portrait of Margherita de' Medici
canvas, inv. 1912 no. 298
post 1646

III-10
Giovanni da San Giovanni
Christ served by the Angels
copper, inv. 1890 no. 1529
c. 1623–1624
doc. in 1701; doc. at Palazzo Pitti in 1928

III-11
Carlo Antonio Sacconi
Portrait of the Servite Friar Giunta
canvas, inv. 1890 no. 1582
doc. in 1794; doc. at Palazzo Pitti in 1928
GPF. M (1713)

III-12
Bronzino's studio
Portrait of Cosimo I de' Medici
wood panel, inv. 1912 no. 212
c. 1560
L. M (1675)

III-13
Cesare Dandini
Portrait of a Man
canvas, inv. 1890 no. 2189
c. 1639

III-14
German school, 16th century
Portrait of a Man
wood panel, inv. 1912 no. 334
dated 1533
doc. at Palazzo Pitti in 1854

III-15
Giulio Cesare Procaccini
Adoration of the Shepherds
wood panel, inv. 1912 no. 319
c. 1604
doc. at Palazzo Pitti in 1828

IV-1
Lavinia Fontana
Portrait of Isabella Ruini (?)
canvas, inv. OdA 1911 no. 536
signed and dated 1593
doc. at Palazzo Pitti in 1828

IV-2
Alessandro Allori's studio
Portrait of a Woman
wood panel, inv. 1912 no. 328
c. 1580
doc. at Palazzo Pitti in 1828

IV-3
Giovanni da San Giovanni
Painting depicting Fame
fresco on slate, inv. 1890 no. 1533
c. 1634
signed
doc. at Palazzo Pitti in 1928
GPF. M

IV-4
Florentine school (?),
16th century
*Portrait of Maria
de' Medici*
canvas, inv. Poggio Impe-
riale no. 393
c. 1581–1582
doc. in 1626

IV-5
Frans Pourbus the
Younger
*Portrait of Elizabeth
of France*
canvas, inv. 1890 no. 2403
c. 1611–1612

IV-6
Onorio Marinari (?)
David and Goliath
copper, inv. 1890 no. 1555
doc. in 1796; doc. at Palazzo Pitti in 1928
DL. M (1649)

IV-7
Livio Mehus
*St. Mary Magdalene
Penitent*
copper, inv. OdA 1911
no. 516
c. 1660–1670
signed: Livio Mehus
doc. at Palazzo Pitti in 1701
GPF. M (1701)

IV-8
Giovanni da San
Giovanni
*Venus combing Cupid's
Hair*
canvas, inv. 1890 no. 2123
1627
DL. M

This painting was commis-
sioned by Don Lorenzo de'
Medici for his own Villa at
Castello and like the *First
Night of Marriage* by the
same artist (II-6), it was
done in 1627, as revealed
by the inscription with the
artist's name on the back
of the canvas. In an irrev-
erent parody from ancient

IV-8

mythology it shows the goddess passing a fine-tooth
comb for nits through the
young Cupid's hair, a task
which must have been very
common in the seventeenth
century.

IV-9
Florentine school,
16th century
*Portrait of Bianca
Cappello*
wood panel, inv. 1890
no. 2317

IV-10
Frans Pourbus the
Younger
*Portrait of Louis XIII
of France*
canvas, inv. 1890 no. 2400
c. 1611 (?)
L. M (1675)

IV-11
Venetian school,
16th century
*Portrait of a Man
(once identified as
Antonio Carracci)*
wood panel, inv. 1912
no. 250
L. M

IV-12
Livio Mehus
*St. Mary Magdalene in
Ecstasy*
copper, inv. OdA 1911
no. 517
c. 1660–1670
signed: Livio Mehus
doc. at Palazzo Pitti in 1701
GPF. M (1701)

Room of the Fine Arts (Sala delle Belle Arti)

In the seventeenth century this room was the "Gentlemen's Antechamber" (Anticamera dei Gentiluomini) in Grand Duchess Vittoria della Rovere's apartment, now known as the "Volterrano Wing". At the beginning of the nineteenth century the Bourbons and then the Lorraines changed this room and the ones around it completely and had them redecorated in a neoclassical style by a group of artists. One artist in particular, Domenico Podestà, is worth mentioning for his work on the ceiling, which he completed in 1817 after the return of the Lorraines to the Tuscan throne with a depiction of *Jupiter sending Iris, Minerva and the Arts to Earth*.

Wall I

I-1
Federico Barocci
Our Lady of the Assumption
paper affixed to wood panel, inv. 1912 no. 261
ante 1582–1584
doc. in 1713–1723
L. M (1675)

I-2
Flemish school, 16th century
Portrait of a Man
wood panel, inv. 1912 no. 424
c. 1509–1510
doc. at Palazzo Pitti in 1828

I-3
Maso da San Friano
Portrait of a Woman
wood panel, inv. 1912 no. 283
doc. at Palazzo Pitti in 1828

I-5

I-4
Florentine school,
16th century
Portrait of a Man
wood panel, inv. 1912 no. 274
c. 1570–1580

I-5
Peter Paul Rubens
Resurrected Christ
canvas, inv. OdA 1911
no. 479
GPF. M

The origin of this painting is
unknown though it can be
dated to 1615–1616. It shows
Christ in the foreground on
the tomb with a powerful
physique reminiscent of
ancient statuary. It was
documented in 1713 in the
collection of Grand Prince
Ferdinando and it is thought
to have come to him from
his brother-in-law, the Elector Palatine of Dusseldorf.
The Elector Palatine owned
a great number of works by
Rubens including a *Portrait
of Isabella Brandt* which he
gave to the Medici Prince
(now on display in the Uffizi
Gallery).

I-6
Carlo Dolci
*Vision of
St. Louis of Toulouse*
canvas, inv. 1890 no. 747
c. 1681–1686
doc. in 1784; doc. at Palazzo Pitti in 1928
GPF. M (1688)

Wall II
II-1
Cigoli
*Virgin teaching the
Infant Jesus to read*
canvas, inv. 1912 no. 430
c. 1595
doc. at Palazzo Pitti from 1732
C. M

II-2
Cristofano Allori
Adoration of the Magi
canvas, inv. 1890 no. 8741
doc. in 1638

This large painting, left
incomplete by the artist
when he died in 1621, is
documented a short time
later in 1638 as being part

II-2

27

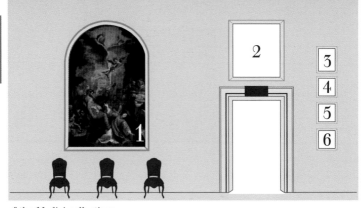

of the Medici collections, where it presumably arrived under Grand Duke Ferdinando II de' Medici. Little is known about why it remained in the artist's studio, or its intended destination, though it may have been done in 1611 either for the Sanctuary of Fontenuova at Monsummano near Pistoia or for an altar in Pisa Cathedral.

II-3
Cigoli
St. Francis praying
canvas, inv. 1912 no. 46
c. 1600
initialled: L.C.
L. M (1675)

Wall III

III-1
Cigoli
*Martyrdom of
St. Stephen*
canvas, inv. 1890 no. 8713
This painting is signed and dated 1597 on the base of the capital in the foreground. It was commissioned for the Florentine nuns of Montedomini by Zaccaria Tondelli, the keeper of the convent, who is in all likelihood depicted on the bottom left. The work portrays the stoning of the Deacon Saint, the first Christian martyr, in a scenographic and evocative manner using a

III

28

colour palette reminiscent of Venetian painting. It is one of Cigoli's masterpieces, and a fundamental point of reference for Florentine painting in the seventeenth century.

III-2
Jacopo Ligozzi
St. Catherine of Alexandria carried by Angels to Mount Sinai
canvas, inv. 1890 no. 8044
signed and dated 1617

III-3
Federico Barocci
Angel of the Annunciation
paper affixed to wood panel, inv. 1912 no. 251
ante 1582–1584
doc. in 1713–1723
L. M (1675)

III-4
Lavinia Fontana (?)
Portrait of a Woman
copper, inv. 1912 no. 433
c. 1600–1605
L. M (1675)

III-5
Justus Suttermans
Portrait of Vittoria della Rovere as St. Margaret
copper, inv. 1890 no. 1038
c. 1639

III-6
Giulio Romano (?)
Holy Family
wood panel, inv. 1912 no. 247
c. 1512
doc. at Palazzo Pitti in 1635
V. DR (1631); GPF. M (1687)

Wall IV

IV-1
Empoli
Madonna del Soccorso (Madonna of Help)
wood panel, inv. 1890 no. 9383
signed and dated 1593
doc. in 1958

IV-2
Jacopo Ligozzi
Vision of St. Francis of Assisi
canvas, inv. 1912 no. 289
signed and dated 1618
doc. in 1618; doc. at Palazzo Pitti in 1828

Room of the Ark (Sala dell'Arca)

In Medicean times this room was an audience chamber in the Grand Duchess' apartment with access to the seventeenth-century chapel of Maria Magdalena of Austria.

It takes its name from the fresco which runs around the walls in a continuous sculpted frieze depicting the *Procession of David with the Ark of the Covenant*. This frieze was done in 1816 by the Milanese artist Luigi Ademollo, a leading figure in early Italian neoclassicism. The commission for the work came from Grand Duke Ferdinand II of Hapsburg Lorraine, who chose to evoke this biblical figure upon his return from exile after the end of Napoleonic rule.

Francesco Carradori
Jupiter Serapis
1784–1785
marble, inv. OdA. no. 882
PL. AL

This bust was inspired by the colossal *Serapis* from the Roman era now on display in the Vatican Museums. The artist gave the work to Grand Duke Peter Leopold of Hapsburg Lorraine, who had it placed in Palazzo Pitti. It was conceived, like the original, to be placed high up, encircled with rays of golden metal which have now been lost.

Chapel of the Relics (Cappella delle Reliquie)

In Medici times this chapel was part of the Grand Duchesses' apartment. It was also the main chapel of the Palace until the neoclassical Palatine Chapel was consecrated on the Ammannati Courtyard in 1785.

Between 1632 and 1784 the relics used for the devotion of the reigning family and others alike were kept in this chapel, and even today the Chapel of the Relics is the most important place of worship in the Grand Ducal apartments. It was built by Alfonso Parigi in 1565, and then renovated for Grand Duchess Maria Magdalena of Austria; during these renovations Michelangelo Cinganelli decorated the chapel around 1612 with frescoes depicting the *Stories of Mary and Mary Magdalene*, from designs by Bernardino Poccetti.

The stuccoes on the walls and the relics cabinets were renovated in 1712, although the doors of the cabinets hold scenes from around 1618 painted by some Florentine artists. These works include an *Annunciation* by Fabrizio Boschi, an *Assumption of Mary Magdalene* and *St. Francis of Assisi* by Matteo Rosselli, a *St. Cosmas and Damian* by Giovanni Bilivert, and a *Baptism of Christ* by Filippo Tarchiani.

On the altar

During the modern era the original altarpiece with the Madonna and Child, now lost, was replaced with the *Rest on the Flight into Egypt* by Battistello Caracciolo from 1618 (inv. OdA 1911 no. 420). Giuseppe Collignon painted the lunette above with *God the Father* in 1821.

On the left

Grazioso Spazzi
Isaac on the Wood Pyre
marble, inv. OdA 1911 no. 422
signed and dated 1860

On the right

Carlo Dolci
God the Father
wood panel, inv. 1890 no. 8688
1667
This painting on wood comes from the Florentine Compagnia dello Scalzo, an Order instituted in 1376 and called 'dello Scalzo' because the monks went barefoot. The work arrived in the Grand Ducal collections in 1785.

Room of the Glass Cases (Sala delle Vetrine)

This small room next to the Room of the Ark holds glass display cases full of precious miniatures, which are the fruits of the patronage and collecting habits of the Della Rovere and Medici families. Some noteworthy items include the set by Giovanna Garzoni (which is worth mentioning both for the quantity and quality of the pieces), the miniatures by Sister Veronica Vitelli, and the two sets by Valerio Mariani and Simonzio Lupi with small paintings belonging to the Electress Palatine Anna Maria Luisa de' Medici.

Wall I

I-1
German school (?),
17th–18th century (after Luis de Morales?)
Ecce Homo
vellum, inv. 1890 no. 7897
c. 1691–1716
doc. at Palazzo Pitti in 1743
AML. M (1691–1716)

I-2
German school (?),
17th–18th century
Adoration of the Shepherds
vellum, inv. OdA 1911 no. 403
c. 1691–1716
doc. at Palazzo Pitti in 1743
AML. M (1691–1716)

I-3
Michael Posner
copy of the *Electress Palatine in Mourning Dress* by Jan Frans van Douven

vellum, inv. 1890 no. 8121
signed and dated 1717
AML. M (1717)

I-4
German school (?),
17th–18th century
(after Marten van Heemskerck ?)
Salvator Mundi
vellum, inv. OdA 1911 no. 407
c. 1691–1716
doc. at Palazzo Pitti in 1743
AML. M (1691–1716)

I-5
German school (?),
17th–18th century
copy of *Christ healing the Paralytic* by Anton van Dyck
vellum, inv. 1890 no. 614
c. 1691–1716
doc. at Palazzo Pitti in 1743
AML. M (1691–1716)

I-6
Michael Posner
copy of the *Noli Me Tangere* by Federico Barocci
vellum, inv. 1890 no. 857
c. 1714–1717
signed
AML. M (1717)

I-7
German school (?),
17th–18th century
copy of *Christ and the Penitent Sinners* by Rubens
vellum, inv. OdA 1911 no. 404
c. 1691–1716
doc. at Palazzo Pitti in 1743
AML. M (1691–1716)

I-8
J. Jakob Buechoffer
copy of the *Battle of the Amazons* by Rubens
1890 no. 842
signed
AML. M (1717)

Wall II

II-1
Richard van Orley
Sacrifice to Apollo
vellum, inv. OdA 1911
no. 867

This piece is part of a series of eight miniatures belonging to the Electress Palatine Anna Maria Luisa de' Medici. She probably commissioned the works from the Belgian artist during his stay in Germany, and then brought them back to Florence in 1717 when she became a widow. This piece and four others (cf. II-2, 4, 5, 7)

hold the signature of the miniaturist.

II-2
Richard van Orley
Pan and Syrinx
vellum, inv. OdA 1911
no. 869
signed

II-3
Richard van Orley
Sacrifice of Iphigenia
vellum, inv. OdA 1911
no. 864

II-4
Richard van Orley
Cecrop's Daughters discover Erichthonius

vellum, inv. OdA 1911
no. 871
signed

II-5
Richard van Orley
Sacrifice to Venus
vellum, inv. OdA 1911
no. 868
signed

II-6
Pieter Boy (?) (after Adriaen van der Werff)
Rest on the Flight into Egypt
enamelled gold plate,
inv. 1890 no. 811
post 1702

II-1

33

C III. M (1706); AML. M (1737)

II-7
Richard van Orley
Sacrifice to Bacchus
vellum, inv. OdA 1911
no. 866

II-8
Richard van Orley
Daphnis and Chloe
vellum, inv. OdA 1911
no. 870

II-9
Richard van Orley
Hymenaios
vellum, inv. OdA 1911
no. 865

II-10
Giovanna Garzoni
Still Life with a Bowl of Peaches and Plums
vellum, inv. 1890 no. 4761
This miniature and the following nineteen works are real masterpieces of naturalistic and botanical painting. They were done in Rome between 1651 and 1662 by the miniaturist from Ascoli for Grand Duke Ferdinando II de' Medici. The set was documented in 1692 in the inventory of the Villa of Poggio Imperiale among the works of art belonging to Grand Duchess Vittoria della Rovere. It is also the most important set in the collection both in terms of quantity and quality.

II-11
Giovanna Garzoni
Still Life with a Bowl of Strawberries, Pears and a Grasshopper
vellum, inv. 1890 no. 4758

II-12
Giovanna Garzoni
Still Life with a Plate of Figs, Jasmines and Pears
vellum, inv. 1890 no. 4757

II-2

II-2

II-13
Giovanna Garzoni
Still Life with a Plate of Peaches and a Cucumber
vellum, inv. 1890 no. 4763

II-14
Giovanna Garzoni
Still Life with a Plate of Grapes, Jujubes and a Peach
vellum, inv. 1890 no. 4748

II-15
Giovanna Garzoni
Still Life with a Chinese Plate, Artichokes, a Rose and Strawberries
vellum, inv. 1890 no. 4760

II-16
Giovanna Garzoni
Still Life with a Plate of Peas and two Roses
vellum, inv. 1890 no. 4762

II- 17
Giovanna Garzoni
Still Life with a Plate of Plums, Jasmines and Hazelnuts
vellum, inv. 1890 no. 4766

II-18
Giovanna Garzoni
Still Life with a Plate of Cherries and two Carnations
vellum, inv. 1890 no. 4764

II-19
Giovanna Garzoni
Still Life with a Plate of Figs and two Sorb Apples
vellum, inv. 1890 no. 4767

II-20
Giovanna Garzoni
Still Life with a Plate of Cherries, Medlars and Figs
vellum, inv. 1890 no. 4747

II-21
Giovanna Garzoni
Still Life with a Split-Open Melon and a Slice of Watermelon
vellum, inv. 1890 no. 4771

II-22
Giovanna Garzoni
Still Life with a Plate of Green Almonds and a Rose
vellum, inv. 1890 no. 4749

II-23
Giovanna Garzoni
Still Life with Fruit, Vegetables, Food, a Dog and an Old Man with Hens (The Man from Artemino)
vellum, inv. 1890 no. 4778
L. M (1648); V. DR (1691)

II-24
Giovanna Garzoni
Still Life with a Plate of Broad Beans and a Carnation
vellum, inv. 1890 no. 4765

II-25
Giovanna Garzoni
Still Life with a Plate, a Pomegranate, Chestnuts, a Snail and a Grasshopper
vellum, inv. 1890 no. 4759

II-26
Giovanna Garzoni
Still Life with a Plate of Pears, Medlars, Cherries and Almonds
vellum, inv. 1890 no. 4772

II-27
Giovanna Garzoni
Still Life with a Plate of Plums, Bindweed, Jasmines and a Walnut
vellum, inv. 1890 no. 4751

II-28
Giovanna Garzoni
Still Life with Grapes, Pears and a Snail
vellum, inv. 1890 no. 4769

II-29
Giovanna Garzoni
Still Life with a Chinese Bowl, Figs, Cherries and a Goldfinch
vellum, inv. 1890 no. 4750

II-30
Giovanna Garzoni
Portrait of a Dog with Bread and a Chinese Cup
vellum, inv. 1890 no. 4770
c. 1648
signed
V. DR (1691)

Wall III

III-1
Herman Hestenburg
Kingfisher
watercolour on paper, inv. 1890 no. 4773
signed
doc. in 1761; doc. at Palazzo Pitti in 1987
C III. M (1700)

III-2
Teresa Berenice Vitelli (Sister Veronica)
Two Sparrows and a Mouse
gouache on vellum, inv. 1890 no. 4774
signed and dated 1720
doc. in 1733
VB. B

III-3
Ferdinando Narvaez
Chinese Porcelain Vase with Flowers
vellum, inv. 1890 no. 6681
signed: Cavaliere Ferdinando Narvaez
VB. B (1732)

III-4
Teresa Berenice Vitelli (Sister Veronica)
Hawfinch with two Cherries and a Vase of Carnations
gouache on vellum, inv. 1890 no. 4755
ante 1706 (?)

III-5
Alessandro Marsili
Bunch of Flowers with Anemones and Tulips
vellum, inv. 1890 no. 6679
signed and dated 1702

III-6
Teresa Berenice Vitelli (Sister Veronica)
Parrot, Great Tit and Two Lizards
gouache on vellum, inv. 1890 no. 4775
signed and dated 1706
doc. in 1761; doc. at Palazzo Pitti in 1987

III-7
Teresa Berenice Vitelli (Sister Veronica)
Bunch of Tulips and Larkspur
gouache on vellum, inv. 1890 no. 4768

1	4	5	8	11	14	17	20 21	25	
2	6	9	12	15	18	22		26	
3	7	10	13	16	19	23	24	27	

Wall IV

IV-1
Simonzio Lupi
St. Francis of Assisi
vellum, inv. 1890 no. 697

This work is part of a series of eleven miniatures attributed to Simonzio Lupi (3 others are on display, cf. IV-4, 5, 15). Lupi was a miniaturist from Bergamo working for the Della Rovere family at the end of the sixteenth century and beginning of the seventeenth century in Duke Francesco Maria della Rovere's 'officinella' (small workshop) in Pesaro. The works in the series can be dated to the 1590s and they were found in one of three illuminated books documented in 1654 in an inventory of the Medici collections. They can be traced back to Vittoria della Rovere's inheritance, where they were documented in 1692.

IV-2
Valerio Mariani
Nativity
vellum, inv. 1890 no. 3510

This work is part of a series of 26 miniatures by the artist from Pesaro (9 others are on display, cf. IV-3, 6, 7, 9, 10, 12, 13, 16, 19). They were previously bound in a small volume for liturgical festivities and dedicated to Francesco Maria II della Rovere, Duke of Urbino. The miniaturist received payments for the volume between 1608 and 1617. It is not clear whether the book was commissioned in 1621 for the nuptials of Federico Ubaldo and Claudia de' Medici, Vittoria della Rovere's parents, as the framed miniatures are documented in 1692 as being part of her inheritance.

IV-3
Valerio Mariani
Nativity of St. John the Baptist
vellum, inv. 1890 no. 688

IV-4
Simonzio Lupi
St. Ubaldo
vellum, inv. 1890 no. 696

IV-5
Simonzio Lupi
St. Egidius
vellum, inv. 1890 no. 700

IV-6
Valerio Mariani
Presentation of Jesus at the Temple
vellum, inv. 1890 no. 3511

IV-1

IV-2

IV-6

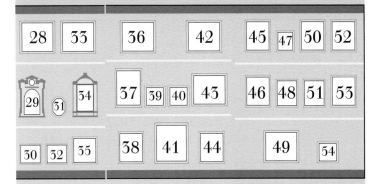

IV-7
Valerio Mariani
Circumcision
vellum, inv. 1890 no. 3507

IV-8
Simonzio Lupi
Resurrection
vellum, inv. 1890 no. 707

This work is one of a se-
ries of ten miniatures undoubtedly by Simonzio Lupi
(4 others are on display,
cf. IV-11, 14, 17, 18). They
are of the same origin as
the set of eleven works by
the artist from Bergamo (cf.
IV-1), and can likewise be
dated to the 1590s.

IV-9
Valerio Mariani
Last Supper
vellum, inv. 1890 no. 3506

IV-10
Valerio Mariani
Nativity of the Virgin
vellum, inv. 1890 no. 680

IV-11
Simonzio Lupi
*Christ and St. Peter on
Lake Tiberias*
vellum, inv. 1890 no. 705

IV-12
Valerio Mariani
*Christ and St. Peter on
Lake Tiberias*
vellum, inv. 1890 no. 690

IV-13
Valerio Mariani
*Martyrdom of
St. Thomas*
vellum, inv. 1890 no. 3504

IV-14
Simonzio Lupi
*Martyrdom of
St. Thomas*
vellum, inv. 1890 no. 712

IV-15
Simonzio Lupi
*St. Raphael Archangel
and Tobias*
vellum, inv. 1890 no. 694

IV-16
Valerio Mariani
*Assumption of the
Virgin*
vellum, inv. 1890 no. 689

IV-17
Simonzio Lupi
Martyrdom of St. Mark
vellum, inv. 1890 no. 711

IV-18
Simonzio Lupi
Crucifixion
vellum, inv. 1890 no. 693

IV-19
Valerio Mariani
Pentecost
vellum, inv. 1890 no. 3500

IV-20
Central European
school (?), 18th century
*Portrait of Emperor
Francesco I*
vellum, inv. OdA 1911
no. 60

IV-21
Central European
school (?), 18th century
*Portrait of Empress
Maria Teresa*
vellum, inv. OdA 1911
no. 61

IV-22
Florentine school,
early 18th century
Glory of the Cross
vellum, inv. 1890 no. 8320
Medici coat of arms in
one of the scenes

IV-23
Central Italian school,
17th century
*Madonna and Child in
a Garden*
vellum, inv. 1890 no. 9644
ante 1616
doc. in 1625

IV-24
Maddalena Corvini
Madonna and Child
vellum, inv. 1890 no. 5574
signed and dated

IV-25
Bernardo Buontalenti (?)
Ascent to Calvary
vellum, inv. 1890 no. 5571
post 1574
doc. in 1692 and in 1695

IV-26
Italian school,
16th century (?)
copy of the *Madonna
of Divine Love* by
Raphael
vellum, inv. 1890 no. 7857
post 1517–1518

IV-27
Florentine school,
17th century
Resurrection
alabaster, inv. OdA 1911
no. 1446
early 17th century
doc. in 1624

IV-28
Leonaert Bramer
(circle) (?)
Carnival Scene
slate, inv. OdA 1911
no. 519
L. M (1675)

IV-29
Roman school,
17th century
*Altar Reliquary with
Annunciation*
lapis lazuli, inv. 1890
no. 9646

IV-30
Reinier Nooms
(Zeeman) (?)
*Seascape with a Three-
Masted Ship at Anchor*
wood panel, inv. 1890
no. 5969
doc. in 1714
C III. M (?); GPF. M

IV-31
Leonaert Bramer
(circle?)
Tavern Scene
slate, inv. OdA 1911
no. 520
L. M (1675)

IV-32
Jacques Stella
*Madonna and Child
with the Young St. John*
Belgian black marble,
inv. 1890 no. 7849
c. 1618–1622

IV-33
Renier Nooms
(Zeeman) (?)
Seascape with a Port
wood panel, inv. 1890
no. 5573
doc. in 1714
C III. M (?); GPF. M

IV-34
Florentine school (?),
17th century
*Godfrey of Bouillon
and St. Louis of France
adoring a Relic of the
Shroud*
vellum, inv. 1890 no. 9645
C. L (1640)

IV-35
Filippo Napoletano
Night Landscape
slate, inv. 1890 no. 715
c. 1617–1621
C II. M

IV-36
Jan van Kessel
*Kitchen Interior with
a Dog*
copper, inv. OdA 1911
no. 523
C III. M (?)

IV-37
Alessandro Turchi
(Orbetto)
Flagellation
slate, inv. Poggio Imperiale no. 2123
1614–1615

IV-38
Leonaert Bramer
*Adoration of the
Shepherds*
slate, inv. 1890 no. 7850
doc. in 1872

IV-39
Florentine school,
17th century
*Stigmata of St. Francis
of Assisi*
landscape stone, inv. 1890
no. 6111

IV-40
Jan van Kessel
*Still Life with Fish on
the Seashore*
copper, 1890 no. 1069
signed and dated 1661
signed on reverse:
Della Sereniss.
Elettrice/I.V.Kessel.F:
doc. at Palazzo Pitti in
1977
AML. M (1731)

IV-41
Leonaert Bramer
Adoration of the Magi
slate, inv. 1890 no. 830
c. 1616–1628
doc. in 1872

IV-42
Jan Asselijn (?)
*Travellers crossing a
Stream at Night*
slate, inv. 1890 no. 1032
signed on reverse:
Krabbeke
doc. in 1704

IV-43
Filippo Napoletano
*Temptations of
St. Anthony Abbot*
landscape stone, inv. 1890
no. 5567
1619
doc. at Palazzo Pitti in
1773

IV-44
Florentine school,
17th century
*St. Mary Magdalene
Penitent*
landscape stone, inv. OdA
1911 no.1440
early 17th century

IV-45
Willem van Mieris the
Younger
*St. Mary Magdalene
Penitent*
wood panel, inv. 1890
no. 1207
signed and dated 1697
doc. in 1772
C III. M ?

IV-46
Frans van Mieris the
Elder
Old Man in Love
wood panel, inv. 1890
no. 1275
1673
doc. in 1704
C III. M (1674)

IV-47
Jan van Kessel
*Still Life with a Monkey
stealing Fruit*
copper, inv. 1890 no. 5576
doc. at Palazzo Pitti in
1828

IV-48
Frans van Mieris the
Elder
Portrait of a Man
wood panel, inv. 1890
no. 1183
signed and dated 1663
signed on reverse:
Francesco Miriis
doc. at Palazzo Pitti in the
early 18th century
GPF. M (1713)

IV-49
F. V. Daellen
Still Life (Vanitas)
wood panel, inv. 1890
no. 1077
C III. M (1686)

IV-50
F. V. Daellen
Still Life (Vanitas)
wood panel, inv. 1890
no. 1081
signed
C III. M (1686)

IV-51
Egbert van
Heemskerck
Old Peasant Woman
wood panel, inv. 1890
no. 1188
c. 1665–1675
doc. at Palazzo Pitti in
1928
L. M

IV-52
Egbert van
Heemskerck
Old Peasant Man
wood panel, inv. 1890
no. 1178
c. 1665–1675
doc. at Palazzo Pitti in
1928
L. M

IV-53
Caspar Netscher
*Young Woman winding
a Clock*
wood panel, inv. 1890
no. 1189
c. 1665
doc. in 1753
GPF. M (1713)

IV-54
Jan van Kessel
*Landscape with Still
Life of Fruit and
Vegetables*
copper, inv. 1890 no. 1228
signed
doc. at Palazzo Pitti in
the second half of the
17th century

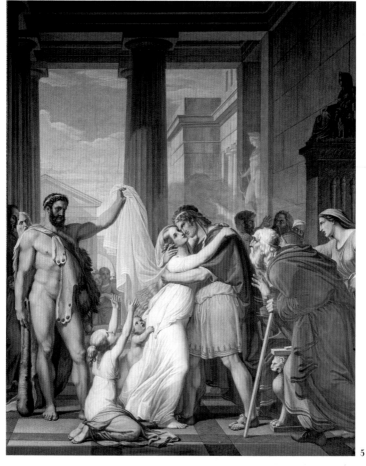

5

Hercules Room (Sala d'Ercole)

In the sixteenth century this room was known as the "Room of the German Guard" (Sala della Guardia Tedesca) and it was part of Vittoria della Rovere's apartment, now known as the "Volterrano Wing". According to plans drawn up by the architect Giuseppe Cacialli, it was transformed into an elegant and scenographic reception room during renovations at the beginning of the nineteenth century. The refined neoclassical decorative work was carried out between 1817 and 1829 by Pietro Benvenuti. The Stories and Labours of Hercules in the five large panels and the ten chiaroscuro compositions on the higher part of the walls are depicted with a magnificence worthy of the vast area which, with its furnishings, provides evidence of the ancient splendours of the royal palace in the Napoleonic and Lorraine eras. Some noteworthy furnishings include a *Clock* on the console table between the two windows belonging to Ferdinand II of Hapsburg Lorraine; this piece is of French manufacture from the eighteenth century and is signed on the dial "Thonissen à Paris". There is also a *Porcelain Vase* of Sèvres manufacture (1784) in the centre of the room with a gilded-bronze mount with figures and festoons; this is the work of Pierre Philippe Thomire and was a gift from Napoleon to Maria Luisa, the Duchess of Lucca.

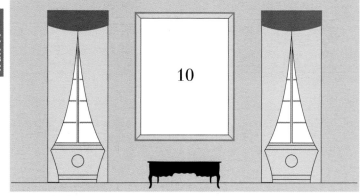

8

11

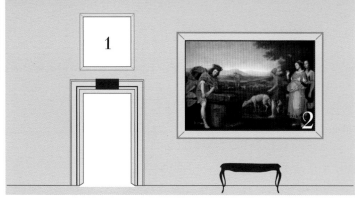

Dawn Room (Sala dell'Aurora)

In the seventeenth century this room was the "Porter's Room" (Camera del Portiere) in an apartment once inhabited by Cardinal Giovan Carlo de' Medici. This whole area of the Palace, now known as the "Volterrano Wing", was completely renovated at the beginning of the nineteenth century under the Bourbons and then the Lorraines. During the renovations after the Lorraines' return, Gaspero Martellini painted the ceiling in 1817–1820 with *Dawn scattering flowers surrounded by the Arts, Time and a Bust of Grand Duke Ferdinand II of Lorraine*.

Wall I

I-1
Justus Suttermans
Portrait of Ivan Czomodanoff
canvas, inv. 1890 no. 2371
1657
GPF. M (1713)

I-2
Lorenzo Lippi
Jacob and Rachel at the Well
canvas, inv. 1890 no. 3476 and no. 3477
doc. in 1677; doc. at Palazzo Pitti in 1928

This painting is the counterpart of the *Triumph of David* (III-1) and shows Rachel with her flock meeting Jacob, before she becomes his favourite wife. Both works were done between 1640 and 1645 and are documented in 1677 by Giovanni Cinelli as being in the Passerini-Galli family house in Florence.

I-2

They were bought by the families' descendents in 1910 and came to Palazzo Pitti in 1928.

Wall II

II-1
Volterrano
Ecce Homo
canvas, inv. Poggio Imperiale no. 747
c. 1680–1683
GPF. M

1

2

4

3

5

II-2
Justus Suttermans
*Portrait of Maria
Magdalena of Austria
as St. Mary Magdalene*
canvas, inv. 1890 no. 563
c. 1625–1630
doc. in 1681; doc. at Palazzo Pitti in 1687

II-3
Empoli
*St. Ivo, Protector of
Widows and Orphans*
wood panel, inv. 1890
no. 1569
signed and dated 1616
C II. M (1616)

This large altarpiece depicts a thirteenth-century ecclesiastical judge, St. Ivo of Brittany, representing his clients. It was done in 1616, as shown by the long dedicatory inscription with the artist's name, for the Court Room of the ancient Magistratura dei Pupilli; this was a communal institution situated in the Uffizi from the sixteenth century which provided judges and notaries to administer the property of orphans. The local superintendent, Benedetto Giugni, commissioned the work and is portrayed on the right, turning towards the viewer. The work came to the Uffizi Gallery in 1777 by order of Grand Duke Peter Leopold of Hapsburg Lorraine and was later transferred to Palazzo Pitti

II-4
Jacopo Ligozzi
Adoration of the Magi
canvas, inv. 1890 no. 8671
signed and dated 1597
doc. in 1808; doc. at Palazzo Pitti from 1928

II-5
Domenico Pugliani
Scene of Birth
wood panel, inv. 1890
no. 8416
c. 1615
doc. in 1920

II-3

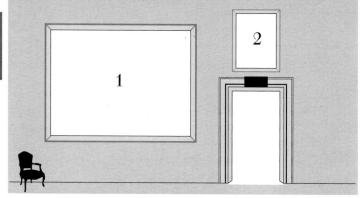

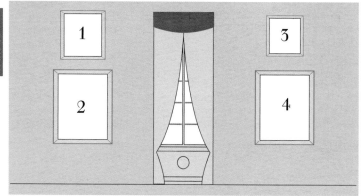

III-1
Lorenzo Lippi
Triumph of David
canvas, inv. 1890 no. 3476
and no. 3477
c. 1640–1645
doc.1677; at Palazzo Pitti
from 1928

III-2
Lavinia Fontana
*Portrait of Francesco
Panigarola*
canvas, inv. 1890 no. 807
signed and dated 1585
doc. at Palazzo Pitti in
1702–1710

IV-1
Pietro da Cortona
*Death of St. Mary
Egyptian*
canvas, inv. 1890 no. 572
c. 1637
C III. M (1674); V. DR
(1692)

IV-2
Jacopo Vignali
*Ruggiero found by
Leone and Melissa*
canvas, inv. 1890 no. 5054
1636
C. M (1636)

IV-3
Jacopo Vignali
*Jesus and the
Samaritan Woman*
canvas, inv. 1890 no. 8030
c. 1620

IV-4
Empoli
Drunkenness of Noah
canvas, inv. 1890 no. 9413
c. 1615–1620
doc. in 1959

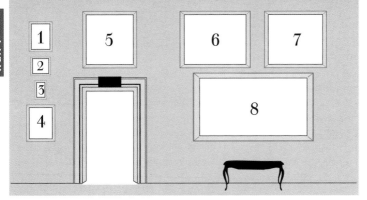

Berenice Room (Sala di Berenice)

In the seventeenth century this room was called the "Gentlemen's Antechamber" (Anticamera dei Gentiluomini) and it was used as Cardinal Giovan Carlo de' Medici's manservant's bedroom. It is in a part of the Palace now referred to as the "Volterrano Wing", which was completed renovated at the beginning of the nineteenth century under the Bourbons and then the Lorraines. During the renovations which took place after the Lorraines' return, Giuseppe Bezzuoli decorated the ceiling in 1820 with *Titus abandoning Berenice* and the lunettes with the *Cardinal Virtues (Temperance, Justice, Fortitude* and *Prudence)*.

Wall I

I-1
Francesco Cambi
Portrait of Stefano della Bella
canvas, inv. 1890 no. 1541
doc. in 1798
written on the reverse:
Ritratto del Signor Stefano della Bella di mano del Signore Francesco Cambi famosissimo pittore fiorentino fatto in Parigi l'anno del nostro Signore MDCXXXVI (Portrait of Signor Stefano della Bella by the hand of Signore Francesco Cambi a highly renowned Florentine painter done in Paris in the year of our Lord MDCXXXVI)
L. M (?)

I-2
Francesco Albani's studio
St. Peter freed from Prison
copper, inv. 1912 no. 278
doc. at Palazzo Pitti in 1836
L. M (1675)

I-3
Volterrano
St. Catherine of Siena
wood panel, inv. 1890 no. 1518
c. 1680–1683
written on the reverse:
Baldassare Franceschini Volterrano
GPF. M (1685)

I-4
Carlo Dolci
Oration in the Garden
wood panel, inv. 1912 no. 288
doc. at Palazzo Pitti in 1761

I-5
Luca Giordano
Adoration of the Magi
canvas, inv. Poggio Imperiale no. 155
doc. at Palazzo Pitti in 1761
C III. M (1688)

I-6
Filippo Tarchiani
Novice receiving her Habit from the Virgin Mary
canvas, inv. 1890 no. 2167
1608–1615
doc. in 1795; doc. at Palazzo Pitti in 1876

I-7
Giovanni Bilivert
Angelica and Ruggiero
canvas, inv. 1890 no. 8034
c. 1623–1624
doc. at Palazzo Pitti in 1987
C. M

I-8
Francesco Furini
Adam and Eve in the Garden of Eden
canvas, inv. 1912 no. 426
c. 1634–1635
F III. AL (1818)

Wall II

II-1
Cristofano Allori
*St. Mary Magdalene
Penitent*
canvas, inv. 1890 no. 2174
C. M

II-2
Orazio Riminaldi
*Martyrdom of
St. Cecilia*
canvas , inv. 1912 no. 489
c. 1620–1625
doc. at Palazzo Pitti in 1970
GPF. M (1693)
This painting is one of
the artist's masterpieces.
It was done between 1620
and 1625 for the Church of
Santa Maria della Rotonda
in Rome (the Pantheon) but
ended up in the Church
of Santa Caterina in Pisa,
where it was brought to the
attention of Grand Prince
Ferdinando de' Medici. The
Medici Prince managed to
obtain the work for his collection in 1693 when he had
it enlarged on three sides
by the painter Gabbiani and
fitted with a new frame. It
shows the beheading of
St. Cecilia, the patron saint
of musicians, who can be
identified by the attributes
of the violin and the score.

II-3
Livio Mehus
Miracle of St. Zenobius

canvas, inv. Poggio
Imperiale no. 1216
c. 1665–1670
L. M (1675)

Wall III

III-1
Cristofano Allori
*Adoration
of the Shepherds*
canvas, inv. 1912 no. 475
c. 1600
doc. at Palazzo Pitti in
1828

III-2
Anton Domenico
Gabbiani
Death of St. Joseph
canvas, inv. Poggio Impe-
riale no. 1029
c. 1726
C III. M

III-3
Giovanni Bilivert
*Joseph and
Potiphar's Wife*
canvas, inv. 1890 no. 1585
signed and dated 1619
doc. in 1779
C. M (1619)

II

IV

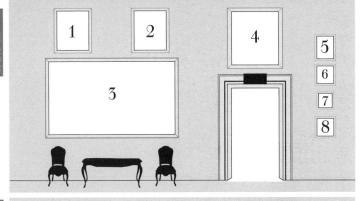

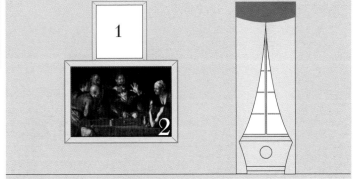

III-4
Francesco Furini
Painting and Poetry
canvas, inv. 1890 no. 6466
signed and dated 1626
doc. at Palazzo Pitti in 1973

III-5
Cristofano Allori
St. Francis Praying
copper, inv. 1912 no. 290
doc. at Palazzo Pitti in
1716–1723
C. M (1666); GPF. M

III-6
Orazio Samacchini
*Mystical Marriage
of St. Catherine of
Alexandria*
wood panel, inv. 1912
no. 240
1560–1565
doc. at Palazzo Pitti in 1828

III-7
after Hans von Aachen
Holy Family
canvas, inv. 1912 no. 284

III-8
Carlo Dolci
St. Simon
canvas, inv. 1890 no. 1557
ante 1664
doc. in 1777; doc. at Palazzo Pitti in 1828

Wall IV

IV-1
Giovanni Bilivert
*Holy Family with the
Young St. John*
wood panel, inv. 1890
no. 2177
signed and dated 1635
doc. in 1784
C. M (1635)

IV-2
Caravaggio (?)
The Tooth Drawer
canvas, inv. 1890 no. 5682
doc. at Palazzo Pitti in 1638

This painting shows the ex-
traction of a tooth with some
commoners standing by and
is depicted with strong light
and dark tones and incisive,
vivid naturalism. It has been
at Palazzo Pitti since 1638,
documented as a work by
Caravaggio and recorded as
such by Scannelli in 1657,
although the painting's attribution to Merisi has been
the subject of some debate.
Many of the historians who
believe it is an original composition have identified it as
the artist's late work from
1600 to 1610, either from
his Maltese-Sicilian period
or his second Neapolitan
period.

Psyche Room (Sala di Psiche)

In the seventeenth century this room was known as the "Winter Room" (Camerino dell'Inverno) in an apartment which was once inhabited by Cardinal Giovan Carlo de' Medici. It is in a part of the Palace now referred to as the "Volterrano Wing", which was completely renovated at the beginning of the nineteenth century under the Bourbons and then the Lorraines. The ceiling was painted with *Cupid taking Psyche to Olympus* by Giuseppe Collignon after 1815 when the Lorraines returned from exile. This room holds the largest single collection of works by the Neapolitan artist Salvator Rosa, who stayed in Florence from 1640 to 1649 working for the Medici family.

Wall I

I-1
Salvator Rosa
Philosopher (Diogenes?) seated in a Wood
pen and brown ink with heightening on wood
inv. GDSU no. 19151
c. 1646–1647
GPF. M (1713)

I-2, I-3
Salvator Rosa
Two Men in a Landscape
Man seated in a Landscape
pen and brown ink with heightening on wood
inv. GDSU no. 19149 and no. 19150
c. 1646–1647
GPF. M (1713)

I-4

I-4
Salvator Rosa
The Philosophers' Wood
canvas, inv. 1912 no. 470
signed
doc. in 1677
F III. AL (1818)
This painting is signed "ROSA" on a stone on the bottom left and can be dated to between 1641–1642 at the beginning of the artist's Florentine period (thanks to the evident influence of Claude Lorrain). It depicts the philosopher Diogenes throwing away his bowl when he sees a young man drinking with his hands from the fountain. Rosa painted this scene for the Gerini family of Florence, before Grand Duke Ferdinand II of Hapsburg Lorraine bought it from them for the Palatine Gallery in 1818.

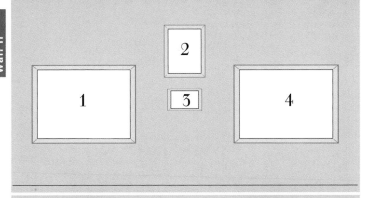

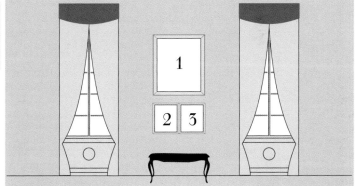

PSYCHE ROOM

Wall II

II-1
Salvator Rosa
*Landscape with a
Bridge (The Broken
Bridge)*
canvas, inv. 1912 no. 306
c. 1645
F III. AL (1820)

II-2
Salvator Rosa
*Natural Arch with a
Waterfall*
canvas, inv. 1890 no. 1319
c. 1640–1642
initialled: SR
doc. at Palazzo Pitti in
1828
L. M (1675)

II-3
Salvator Rosa
*Harbour Scene with
Fortifications and a
Natural Arch*
canvas, inv. 1890 no. 1325
c. 1640–1649
F III. AL (1820)

II-4
Salvator Rosa
*Seascape with Ships
and Ruins (Seascape
with Towers)*
canvas, inv. 1912 no. 306
and no. 312
c. 1645
F III. AL (1820)

Wall III

III-1
Salvator Rosa
*Empedocles leaping
into Etna*
pen and brown ink with
heightening on wood
inv. GDSU no. 19152
c. 1646–1647
GPF. M (1713)

III-2, III-3
Salvator Rosa
*Landscape with a Tree
and a Figure
Landscape with a Tree
and a Standing Figure*
pen and brown ink with
heightening on wood
inv. GDSU no. 19173 and
no. 19174
c. 1648–1649
GPF. M (1713)

Wall IV

IV-1

Salvator Rosa
Battle Scene
canvas, inv. 1912 no. 133
signed
F II. M

This painting is signed with the anagram "SARO" on the shield on the bottom left where the artist has depicted himself as a young man. It is thought to be the first work he carried out in Tuscany between 1640 and 1641 presumably on a commission from Grand Duke Ferdinando II, who took the artist under his protection. The scene probably shows a fictional battle, a genre that artists such as Borgognone focussed on and which became very popular with collectors in the seventeenth and eighteenth centuries.

IV-

52

Music Room (Sala della Musica)

This room was created at the beginning of the nineteenth century by the union of two rooms which, in the seventeenth century, were used as the Grand Duchess' resting room and as the antechamber between her apartment and that of the Grand Duke. During the Napoleonic era in 1813, plans were made to turn the room into "Napoleon's main drawing room" and to decorate it with wall paintings depicting the *Genius of France* and Napoleon's battles. When the Lorraine family returned in 1814 the room, then incomplete, was decorated instead by Luigi Ademollo with the *Glory of the House of Hapsburg* and intended for musical performances. The musical theme is evoked by the appliqués in the shape of horns and the stools and side tables in the shape of drums. In 1860, when Italy was unified and the Savoy family came to power, the decorations were modified with the addition of the Italian flag and Austria was transformed into Italy with a blue cloak and a Savoy crown. The monochrome frieze remains, however, with the *Liberation of Vienna from the Turkish siege of 1683*.

Some noteworthy pieces in this room include the *Table* by Pierre Philippe Thomire in the centre in finely-wrought gilded bronze and malachite; this piece of furniture was made in Paris (1819) for Count Nicola Demidoff, the Russian ambassador to Tuscany, which he then gave to Grand Duke Leopold II of Lorraine in 1829. There are also *Four busts in marble* portraying Roman emperors; these are copies of ancient originals, most probably by the sculptor Francesco Carradori, and not Giuseppe Piamontini, as it has previously been suggested. The busts are positioned on pedestals made especially for this room in 1821.

Borgognone
Battle of Lützen
Battle of Nördlingen
canvas, inv. OdA 1911
no. 451 and no. 452
M. M (1656)
These two paintings, along with another two now at the Uffizi Gallery in the Vasari Corridor (the *Battle of Mongiovino* and the *Taking of Radicofani*), represent the battles of the Thirty Years War in which Prince Mattias de' Medici took part between 1632 and 1639. The Medici Prince commissioned the works and had them done in 1656 for a Villa at Lappeggi, his country residence.

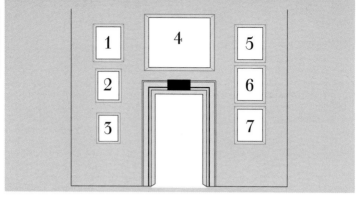

Poccetti Gallery (Galleria del Poccetti)

Formerly a small loggia (loggetta) used as a gallery in the seventeenth century, this area linked the Grand Duke's apartment to that of the Grand Duchess. The pictorial and stucco decoration of the barrel vault and the base of the walls began in 1620 during Cosimo II's reign and was completed five years later under Christine of Lorraine and Maria Magdalena of Austria. Although the work is traditionally attributed to Poccetti, it is actually based on designs by his pupil Michelangelo Cinganelli. These designs were transformed into painting by Filippo Tarchiani, Matteo Rosselli and Ottavio Vannini. *Faith*, *Justice* and *Fortitude* are depicted on the ceiling and the lunettes hold allegories of *Florence* and *Siena*. The loggetta was closed off in 1813 and the room became part of the Palatine Gallery as it is today. The room holds a semi-precious stone *Table* which was made using the "commesso" mosaic inlay technique and set on an ebony base with gilded bronze finishing; it was produced in the Grand Ducal workshops in 1716 from a design by Giovan Battista Foggini (inv. Mobili Artistici no. 1506). There is also a *Bust of Cosimo II de' Medici* by Mattias Ferrucci which was sculpted in porphyry in 1621 (inv. OdA 1911, no. 1814), although it was not thought to be a particularly good likeness of the Grand Duke by his consort Maria Magdalena of Austria.

Wall I

I-1
Andrea Pozzo
Portrait of the Jesuit Father Giovan Pietro Pinamonti
canvas, inv. 1912 no. 496
c. 1703–1704
doc. in 1704; doc. at Palazzo Pitti in 1828

I-2
Domenico Fetti (?)
St. Juliana
canvas, inv. 1890 no. 9262

I-3
Rosso Fiorentino
Portrait of a Man
wood panel, inv. 1912 no. 249
c. 1520–1522
doc. at Palazzo Pitti in 1815

I-4
Bartolomeo Cavarozzi
St. Jerome in his Study
canvas, inv. 1912 no. 417
c. 1617
doc. at Palazzo Pitti in 1638
C II. M.

I-5
Scipione Pulzone's studio
Portrait of Cardinal Ferdinando de' Medici
wood panel, inv. 1912 no. 492
c. 1603–1608
L. M (1675)

I-6
Federico Barocci
Portrait of Monsignor Francesco Prospero Urbani
canvas, inv. 1912 no. 407
ante 1582–1584
doc. in 1624; doc. at

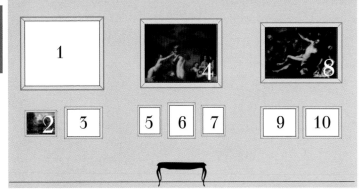

Palazzo Pitti from the end of the 17th century
V. DR (1631)

I-7
after Pieter Paul Rubens
copy of the *Portrait of George Villiers, Duke of Buckingham*
wood panel, inv. 1912 no. 324
L. M. (1675)

Wall II

II-1
Lorenzo Lippi
Three Young Men led to the Furnace

canvas, inv. 1890 no. 3560
c. 1635
doc. from 1911

II-2
Gaspard Dughet
River Landscape
canvas, inv. 1912 no. 416
L II. AL

This painting, along with three other works (II-3, II-9, II-10), was in possession of the artist Fedele Acciai and was bought for Grand Duke Leopold II of Hapsburg Lorraine between 1824 and 1834, when it is documented as being at Palazzo Pitti. Dughet worked in Rome

during the seventeenth century and he completed these works at a late stage in his life. The colonnade of St. Peter's Square, which Bernini completed in 1667, can be seen in the *Landscape with Ruins and Figures* (II-10), thus allowing the work to be dated from the following year onwards.

II-3
Gaspard Dughet
Landscape with a Faun and Nymphs
canvas, inv. 1912 no. 421
doc. at Palazzo Pitti in 1834
L II. AL

II-2

II-4
Francesco Furini
Hylas and the Nymphs
canvas, inv. 1890 no. 3562

The subject of this painting is quite rare, chosen by the buyer Agnolo Galli for whom Furini did the painting between 1630 and 1633. The work is a masterpiece of the artist's early maturity showing his use of strong light and dark tones in the depiction of Hylas, an Argonaut, being kidnapped by the fountain nymphs who had fallen in love with him and then later killed him.

II-5
Domenico Fetti's studio
Parable of the Unjust Steward
wood panel, inv. 1912 no. 26
early 1600s
L. M (1673)

II-6
Jacob Pynas
Sermon of St. John the Baptist
canvas, inv. 1912 no. 431
c. 1603–1608
doc. at Palazzo Pitti from 1675
L. M (1675)

II-7
Domenico Fetti's studio
Parable of the Lost Drachma
early 1600s
wood panel, inv. 1912 no. 30
L. M (1673)

II-8
Jusepe Ribera
Martyrdom of St. Batholomew
canvas, inv. 1912 no. 19

This painting can be dated to between 1620 and 1630 and depicts the flaying of the saint by order of Astrages, the King of Armenia, because he had refused to worship the pagan god

Baldach. This subject was used several times by the Spanish artist and was copied by others, confirming its success; it allowed Ribera to dwell on the realistic representation of anatomical details like the limp skin and calloused hands of the old man with a dramatic use of light, bringing to mind Caravaggio's work during his Neapolitan period.

II-9
Gaspard Dughet
Landscape with Shepherds and their Flocks
canvas, inv. 1912 no. 441
doc. at Palazzo Pitti in 1834
L II. AL

II-10
Gaspard Dughet
Landscape with Ruins and Figures
canvas, inv. 1912 no. 436
doc. at Palazzo Pitti in 1834
L II. AL

II-

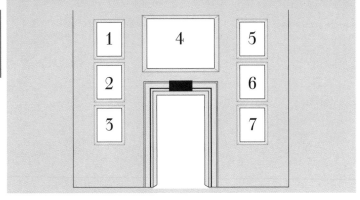

POCCETTI GALLERY

Wall III

Wall III

III-1
Niccolò Cassana
Portrait of a Man
canvas, inv. 1912 no. 481
GPF. M (1713)

III-2
Peter Lely's studio
Portrait of Oliver Cromwell
canvas, inv. 1912 no. 408

III-3
after Pieter Paul Rubens
Portrait of a Woman
canvas, inv. 1890 no. 761
L. M (1675)

III-4
Andrea Schiavone
Adoration of the Shepherds
canvas, inv. 1890 no. 905
doc. at Palazzo Pitti in 1723
L. M. (1675)

III-5
Justus Suttermans
Portrait of General Grifoni (?)
canvas inv. 1912 no. 485
c. 1650
doc. at Palazzo Pitti in 1702–1710

III-6
Niccolò Cassana
Portrait of an Artist
canvas, inv.1912 no. 188
late 17th to early
18th century
GPF. M (1713)

III-7
Jan van Scorel
St. Francis of Assisi receives the Stigmata
wood panel, inv. 1912
no. 482
c. 1520

II-8

57

Prometheus Room (Sala di Prometeo)

Although this room was part of the Grand Duke's private apartment in Medicean times, it was also used for meetings of the Consiglio del Granducato (Council of the Grand Duchy). Once it became part of the new private apartment its ceiling was decorated in a neoclassical style between 1809 and 1814 by the Sienese painter Giuseppe Collignon. The scenes depicted include *Prometheus stealing Fire from Apollo, protected by Minerva*, and monochrome stories about Prometheus next to the *Seasons* in the corners.

When the new Palatine Gallery was created the oldest paintings in the collection from the fifteenth century were placed here, and in particular twelve "tondos" set in neoclassical square frames.

Wall I

I-1
Emilian school (?),
16th century
Allegorical Scene
wood panel, inv. 1890
no. 5064
doc. in 1589

I-2
Florentine school,
16th century
Portrait of a Woman
wood panel, inv. 1912 no. 351
c. 1520
doc. at Palazzo Pitti in 1828

I-3
Francesco Salviati
*Portrait of John of the
Black Bands*
wood panel, inv. 890
no. 5195
CI. M

In 1568 Vasari wrote about Salviati in his *Lives* referring to "a head, or rather, a portrait, of Signor Giovanni de' Medici, the father of Duke Cosimo, which was very beautiful". The painting was thought to be lost, although in 2009 it was identified in storage and restored. It can now rightfully take its place among the most important paintings from the sixteenth century in the Palatine Gallery. The work is a posthumous portrait of the condottiere, who died in 1526, and can be dated to 1546–1548 during the last years of Salviati's residence in Florence.

I-4
Andrea del Minga and
Baccio Bandinelli
*Adam and Eve expelled
from the Garden of Eden*

wood panel, inv. 1912
no. 378
c. 1560
doc. at Palazzo Pitti in
1560–1567

I-5
Pontormo
Adoration of the Magi
wood panel, inv. 1912
no. 379
FI. M

This painting was one of the decorative panels on a high-backed wooden chest in an antechamber in the Benintendi family house in Florence. It was surrounded by four other paintings of the same size including the *St. John the Baptist* by Andrea del Sarto on display in the Jupiter Room (cf. I-7), the *Baptism of Christ* (now in Berlin), the *Legend of the Dead King* by Bachiacca, and the *Bathsheba* by Franciabigio (both in Dresden). The *Bathsheba* bears the date 1523, which can almost certainly be used as a reference for all the paintings.

I-6
Michele di Ridolfo del Ghirlandaio (?)
Portrait of a Woman
wood panel, inv. Poggio a Caiano no. 18
doc. in 1845

I-7
Biagio Pupini
Madonna and Child with the Young St. John
wood panel, inv. 1912 no. 299

I-8
Jusepe de Ribera
St. Francis in Ecstasy
canvas, inv. 1912 no. 73
signed and dated 1643
M. M (1659)

I-9
Girolamo Siciolante da Sermoneta (?)
Holy Family with the Young St. John (Madonna of the Lizard)
wood panel, inv. 1912 no. 57
doc. in 1588; doc. at Palazzo Pitti in 1697
FI. M (1588)

I-3

I-10
Bronzino's studio
Portrait of Cosimo I de' Medici
wood panel, inv. 1912 no. 403
doc. at Palazzo Pitti in 1859

I-11
Ridolfo del Ghirlandaio
Madonna and Child
wood panel, inv. 1912 no. 363
1510–1513

doc. in 1704; doc. at Palazzo Pitti in 1809

I-12
Francesco Salviati (?)
Portrait of a Man
wood panel, inv. 1912 no. 361
c. 1550

I-13
Andrea del Minga and Baccio Bandinelli
Creation of Eve

I-5

wood panel, inv. 1912 no. 367
c. 1560
doc. at Palazzo Pitti in
1560–1567

I-14
Giacinto Gimignani
Rebecca at the Well
wood panel, inv. 1912 no. 368
V. DR (1691)

Wall II

II-1
Master of the Scandicci
Lamentation
*Madonna and Child
with the Young St. John*
wood panel, inv. 1912 no. 199
c. 1509–1512

II-2
Mariotto Albertinelli
Adoration of the Child
wood panel, inv. 1912 no. 365
c. 1498
doc. at Palazzo Pitti in 1761

II-3
Bachiacca
St. Mary Magdalene
wood panel, inv. 1912 no. 102
c. 1530
doc. in 1716–1723

II-4
Santi di Tito
*Portrait of Don
Giovanni de' Medici*
wood panel, inv. 1912 no. 287
c. 1590
signed: ... Santi di Tito F.
doc. at Palazzo Pitti in 1782

II-5
Fruilian friend of
Dosso Dossi
Portrait of a Man
wood panel, inv. 1912 no. 382

II-6
after Bartolomeo
Schedoni
Madonna and Child
wood panel, inv. 1912
no. 360
doc. a Pitti at the end of
the 17th century

II-7
Pontormo
*The Ten Thousand
Martyrs*
wood panel, inv. 1912 no. 182
doc. in 1638

This painting was commissioned by the women of the Ospedale degli Innocenti (Hospital of the Innocents) in 1529–1530 during the siege of Republican Florence. It is thought to depict either the martyrdom of St. Achatius and his men crucified on Mount Ararat or the martyrdom of St. Maurice and the Theban Legion. The composition is divided into several episodes and is full of naked figures. It aims to allude to the Florentines ready to sacrifice themselves defending their freedom, just like the ten thousand martyrs who preferred to die rather than abandon their faith.

II-8
Master of the Borghese
Tondo
Adoration of the Magi
wood panel, inv. 1912 no. 358
doc. at Palazzo Pitti in 1829

II-9
Domenico Beccafumi
*Holy Family with the
Young St. John*
wood panel, inv. 1912 no. 359
c. 1530
doc. at Palazzo Pitti from 1828
A. M (1588)

II-10
Piero di Cosimo
Portrait of a Woman
paper affixed to wood
panel, inv. 1890 no. 604
1500–1505
doc. at Palazzo Pitti in 1928

II-11
Girolamo Siciolante da
Sermoneta (?)
Patience
canvas, inv. 1912 no. 399
L. M (1675)

II-12
Cosimo Rosselli
Adoration of the Child
wood panel, inv. 1912 no. 354
c. 1490
doc. at Palazzo Pitti in 1791

II-13
Naumburg Master (?)
*Madonna and Child
with the Young St. John*
wood panel, inv. 1912 no. 349

II-7

II-14
School of Ferrara,
16th century
*Madonna and Child
with St. Benedict and
St. Andrew*
wood panel, inv. 1912 no. 309

II-15
Fra' Bartolomeo
Ecce Homo
fresco on flat roof tile,
inv. 1912 no. 377
C. M (1666)

II-16
Giovanni Battista
Bertucci
Christ at the Column
wood panel, inv. 1912 no. 369
c. 1500–1505

II-17
Sandro Botticelli
Portrait of a Man
wood panel, inv. 1912 no. 372
Formerly attributed to
Andrea del Castagno, this

II-17

61

portrait of a young man with a hat suffered damage to the facial area when the painting was cleaned in the past. Documented at Palazzo Pitti from 1829, it is, as now acknowledged by historians, the undoubted work of Botticelli. It was done around 1470 at the same time as the *Fortitude* at the Uffizi Gallery, the *Portrait of Esmeralda Brandini* at the Victoria and Albert Museum in London and the *Portrait of a Young Man in Black* at the Louvre.

II-18
Sandro Botticelli
*Portrait of a Woman
(La Bella Simonetta)*
wood panel, inv. 1912
no. 353

The inventory numbers on the back of this portrait attest to the fact that it belonged to the old Medici collections. The attribution of the painting to Botticelli, contested by some, must be reasserted due to the studied grace of the face with its absorbed expression and the elongation of the neck, typical stylistic elements of the maestro. The work can be dated to around 1485.

II-1

II-2

II-19
Sandro Botticelli's
studio, 15ᵗʰ century
Madonna and Child,
Young St. John and the
Archangels Michael
and Gabriel
wood panel, inv. 1912
no. 348

II-20
Luca Signorelli
Holy Family with
St. Catherine of
Alexandria (?)
wood panel, inv. 1912 no. 355
This tondo is a work of the
artist's maturity and can be
dated to around 1490–1492
thanks to its similarity to
the altarpieces at Volterra,
although its origin and prior
ownership is undocument-
ed. It is recorded as being
at the Palatine Gallery from
1828 onwards, and when
it arrived it is thought to
have been bordered by a
square frame, like many
of the other tondos in this
room. This frame was later
substituted with the current
coeval one, which came
from the Convent of San
Marco in 1867.

II-21
Franciabigio
Defamation of Apelles
wood panel, inv. 1912 no. 427
c. 1513
initialled: FBC

III-1
Pseudo Granacci
Madonna and Child
with the Young St. John
and two Angels
wood panel, inv. 1912
no. 342
doc. at Palazzo Pitti in
1828

III-2
Cristofano Allori
Portrait of a Man
canvas, inv. 1912 no. 72
c. 1600–1605

III-3
Jacopo de Boateri
Holy Family
wood panel, inv. 1912
no. 362
signed
doc. at Palazzo Pitti in
1687

III-4
Valerio Marucelli
Assumption
of St. Mary Magdalene
alabaster, inv. 1912
no. 346
1615
doc. in 1637; doc. at Palazzo Pitti in 1834

III-5
Guido Reni (?)
Young Bacchus
canvas, inv. 1912 no. 47
doc. at Palazzo Pitti in 1698
GPF. M (1713)

III-6
Filippo Lippi
Madonna and Child
with the Birth of the
Virgin and Meeting of
Joachim and Anna
wood panel, inv. 1912 no. 343
doc. at Palazzo Pitti in
1761
This painting on wood can
be identified as the tondo
commissioned by Leonardo
Bartolini in 1452 from the
Carmelite monk and artist
when he was about to begin
frescoing the main chapel of
Prato Cathedral. Lippi depicts the Virgin Mary and
her Son in the foreground
with great wisdom and com-
positional balance, while
the background holds the
meeting of Mary's parents,
Joachim and Anna, as well
as the birth of the Virgin.

III-7
Mirabello Cavalori
Portrait of a Man
wood panel, inv. 1912 no. 238

III-8
Francesco Granacci
Holy Family with the
Young St. John
wood panel. inv. 1912 no. 345
c. 1520
doc. at Palazzo Pitti in 1828

63

III-9
Amico Aspertini (?)
Adoration of the Magi
wood panel, inv. 1912
no. 341
c. 1497–1498
L. M (1675)

III-10
Francesco Botticini
*Madonna adoring the
Child with the Young
St. John and Angels*
wood panel, inv. 1912 no. 347
c. 1490
doc. at Palazzo Pitti in
1828
L. M (1675)

III-11
French school,
16th century
Portrait of a Woman
wood panel, inv. 1912 no. 260

III-12
Florentine school,
17th century
Portrait of a Woman
copper, inv. 1912 no. 273

III-13
after Andrea del Sarto
copy of the *Tobias and
the Archangel Raphael*
wood panel, inv. 1912 no. 292
doc. at Palazzo Pitti in 1628

III-14
Venetian school,
16th century
*Portrait of a Man
(Antonio Carracci)*
wood panel, inv. 1912 no. 250
L. M

III-15
Andrea del Sarto
Madonna of Humility
wood panel, inv. OdA
1911 no. 1154
c. 1513–1514
doc. in 1635
A. M. (1621)

Wall IV

IV-1
Sandro Botticelli and studio
Madonna and Child with the Young St. John
canvas, inv. 1912 no. 357

This painting can be traced back to a phase of invention which was full of pathos and spirituality for the maestro. It came during his last years under the influence of Savonarola and is revealed here in this work, translated into painting by his studio around 1505 with a decidedly higher level of quality than many other well-known pieces improperly attributed to Botticelli.

IV-2
Ridolfo del Ghirlandaio (?)
St. Peter and St. Paul
wood panel, inv. 1890 no. 6063
1503
doc. in 1880

IV-3
Jacopo del Sellaio
Adoration of the Child with the Young St. John
wood panel, inv. 1912 no. 364
c. 1490
doc. at Palazzo Pitti in 1828

IV-4
Baldassarre Peruzzi
Apollo and the Muses
wood panel, inv. 1912 no. 167
doc. in 1633; doc. at Palazzo Pitti in 1706
Fl. M (1588)

IV-1

Corridor of the Columns (Corridoio delle Colonne)

In the seventeenth century this room was a terrace above a loggia connecting the Palace's two internal courtyards. During the Lorraine era at the end of the eighteenth century it was converted into the current corridor and adorned with the two alabaster columns from which it takes its name. When it became part of the Palatine Gallery it was decorated between 1828 and 1859 with eight large semi-precious stone *commesso* panels (inlaid mosaics) depicting the *Liberal Arts* and *Roman and Tuscan Views*. Later, a series of small Medici portraits were also added. The current display was mounted in 1912 and is dedicated to small-scale Flemish and Dutch painting.

Wall I from the left

I-1
Hendrick Cornelisz Vroom
Seascape with a three-masted ship and other sailing boats
wood panel, inv. 1890 no. 1055
signed and dated 1631
doc. in 1790
C III. M (1667–1669)?

I-2
Paul Bril
Landscape with Hunters and the Flight into Egypt
canvas, inv. 1890 no. 1126
initialled: PA BRILI
C. M (1666)

I-3
Dutch school, 17th century
Landscape with Venus, Cupid and Satyrs

copper, inv. 1912 no. 461
doc. at Palazzo Pitti in 1834

I-4
Frans Francken II
Allegory of Genius
wood panel, inv. 1890 no. 1061
c. 1610–1615
signed
doc. in 1796

I-5
Cornelis van Poelenburgh
Landscape with Bathers
copper, inv. 1912 no. 460
C II. M

This small painting from around 1620 as well as many others on display here in the corridor, reveal the preference accorded by the Medici court to this Dutch painter at the time of Grand Duke Cosimo II de' Medici. The artist stayed in Italy for ten years from 1617 to 1627 and spent an unknown period

of time in Florence, most probably before the Medici Grand Duke died in 1621. In addition to receiving the Grand Duke's patronage, the artist also painted for the Grand Duke's brother, Cardinal Carlo de' Medici.

I-6
Cornelis van Poelenburgh
Moses saved from the Waters
inv. 1890 no. 1203
copper, doc. at Palazzo Pitti in 1638
C II. M (1638)

I-7
Cornelis van Poelenburgh
Landscape with Shepherd and Goats

Landscape with Ruins and Figures
copper, inv. 1912 no. 317
doc. in 1702
C. M (1666)

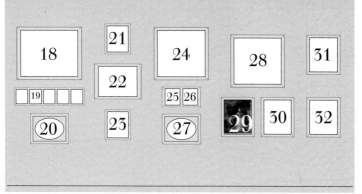

I-8
Cornelis van
Poelenburgh
*Landscape with
Shepherds and a Dancer*
copper, inv. 1912 no. 473
c. 1620
doc. at Palazzo Pitti in 1666
C. M; C III. M

I-9
Cornelis van
Poelenburgh
*Landscape with
Dancing Satyrs*
copper, inv. 1890 no. 1221
doc. at Palazzo Pitti in 1638
C II. M (1638)

I-10
Cornelis van
Poelenburgh
St. Peter
(copper, inv. 1890
no. 8267)
St. Paul
(copper, inv. 1890 no. 8266)
St. John the Evangelist
(copper, inv. 1890 no. 8265)
St. Lawrence
(copper, inv. 1890 no. 8264)
St. Thomas Aquinas (?)
(copper, inv. 1890 no. 1095)
c. 1620
doc. at Palazzo Pitti in 1704
C II. M

I-11
Cornelis van
Poelenburgh
*Landscape with Ruins
and a Shepherd*
wood panel, inv. 1890
no. 1198
doc. in 1702

I-12
Willem van Aelst
Still Life with Birds
canvas, inv. 1890 no. 1209
1652–1653
doc. at Palazzo Pitti in
1928
GC. M; GPF. M

I-5

I-13
Cornelis van
Poelenburgh
*Marshy Landscape
with Ruins and
Herdsmen*
copper, inv. 1890 no. 1195
c. 1617–1627
L. M (1675)

I-14
Cornelis van
Poelenburgh (?)
*Landscape with Ruins
and Shepherds*
copper, inv. 1890 no. 1218
signed: Cornelio Satiro
doc. in 1704; doc. at Palazzo Pitti in 1928
C. M; F II. M

I-15
Cornelis van
Poelenburgh
*Adoration of the
Shepherds*
copper, inv. 1890 no. 1224
post 1627
initialled: C P
doc. in 1773

I-16
Follower of Cornelis
van Poelenburgh
*Landscape with
Nymphs and Satyrs*
canvas, inv. 1890 no. 1307
doc. at Palazzo Pitti in
1800

I-17
Jan de Momper (?)
*Landscape with a
Natural Arch*
copper, inv. 1890 no. 1175
doc. at Palazzo Pitti in 1832

I-18
Cornelis van
Poelenburgh
*Moses striking Water
from the Rock*
copper, inv. 1890 no. 1220
doc. at Palazzo Pitti in 1638
C II. M (1638)

I-?

I-19
Cornelis van
Poelenburgh
Abraham and Isaac
(copper, inv. 1890 no. 8263)
*Tobias and the
Archangel Raphael*
(copper, inv. 1890 no. 8262)
*St. Anna and the Virgin
Mary*
(copper, inv. 1890 no. 8261)
*St. Joseph and the
Infant Jesus*
(copper, inv. 1890 no. 8260)
St. John the Baptist
(copper, inv. 1890 no. 1093)
c. 1620
doc. at Palazzo Pitti in 1704
C II. M

I-20
Cornelis van
Poelenburgh
*Landscape with a
Stream and Figures*
wood panel, inv. 1890
no. 1217
doc. in 1702

I-21
Michelangelo
Cerquozzi
*Two figures in a
Landscape*
copper, inv. 1890 no. 1283
doc. at Palazzo Pitti in
1687
L. M (1675)

I-22
Cornelis van
Poelenburgh
*Landscape with Ruins
and Figures*
copper, inv. 1890 no. 1176
L. M (1675)

I-23
Cornelis van
Poelenburgh (?)
Landscape with Ruins
copper, inv. 1890 no. 1197
signed: Cornelio Satiro
doc. in 1704; doc. at Palazzo Pitti in 1928
C. M; F II. M

I-24
Cornelis van
Poelenburgh
*Landscape with
Dancers among Ruins*
copper, inv. 1890 no. 1200
doc. at Palazzo Pitti in 1638
C II. M (1638)

I-25
Cornelis van
Poelenburgh
*Landscape with an
Angel appearing to a
Woman*
copper, inv. 1890 no. 1094
c. 1620
doc. at Palazzo Pitti in 1702

I-26
Cornelis van
Poelenburgh
*Landscape with a
Grotto in the Roman
Countryside*
copper, inv. 1890 no. 1194
doc. in 1702

I-27
Cornelis van
Poelenburgh
*Landscape with a
Triumphal Arch
and Herdsmen*
copper, inv. 1912 no. 479
c. 1620
doc. at Palazzo Pitti in 1666
C. M; C III. M

I-28
Frans Francken II
*Triumph of Neptune
and Amphitrite*
wood panel, inv. 1890
no. 1068
c. 1610
signed

I-29
Jan Frans van Douven
*Portrait of Anna Maria
Luisa de' Medici*
canvas, inv. 1912 no. 471
Like the other works on
display here, this small
painting was done when
Anna Maria Luisa went to
Düsseldorf in 1691 as the
consort of the Elector Palatine Johann Wilhelm von
der Pfalz, who died in 1716.
The artist often worked for
the Elector Palatine and
portrayed him on horse-
back (inv. 1890 no. 993), in
fancy dress with his consort
(I-32), and the couple dancing together (Inv. OdA 1911
no. 768).

I-30
Jan Frans van Douven
*Portrait of Anna Maria
Luisa de' Medici
Dancing*
canvas, inv. 1912 no. 477
1699
signed and dated 1699
doc. at Palazzo Pitti in
1835–1836
AML. M

I-31
Jan Frans van Douven
*Portrait of Anna Maria
Luisa de' Medici*
canvas, inv. 1912 no. 472
(1890 no. 9157)
c. 1695–1705
doc. at Palazzo Pitti in
1713
AML. M

I-32
Jan Frans van Douven
*Portrait of the Elector
Palatine and his Wife
in Fancy Dress*
canvas, inv. 1912 no. 478
c. 1695–1705
signed
doc. at Palazzo Pitti in
1713
AML. M

II-1
David Ryckaert III
*Temptations of
St. Anthony Abbot*
canvas, inv. 1890 no. 1091
post 1650
doc. in 1753

II-2
Filippo Napoletano
The Mill
copper, inv. 1890 no. 1214
signed: Filippo
Napoletano
c. 1621
C. M. (1666); GPF. M

II-3
Jan Asselijn
*Mountain Landscape
with a Cascade and
Shepherds*
canvas, inv. 1890 no. 1045
initialled: JA
doc. at Palazzo Pitti in
1715
C III. M

II-4
David Ryckaert III
*Temptations of
St. Anthony Abbot*
wood panel, inv. 1890
no. 1144
post 1650
doc. at Palazzo Pitti in
the late 17th to early
18th century

II-5
David Teniers the
Younger (?)
The Alchemist
canvas, inv. 1890 no. 1067
doc. at Palazzo Pitti in
1778

II-6
Paul Bril
*Seascape with Boats
at Anchor*
canvas, inv. 1890 no. 1133
initialled: PA. BRIL II
C. M (1666)

69

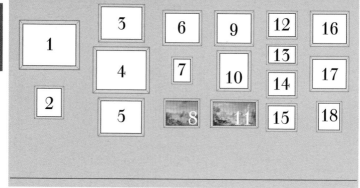

II-7
Flemish school,
16th to 17th century
Landscape with Ruins
copper, inv. 1890 no. 1274
doc. in 1863

II-8
Caspar van Wittel
*View of Rome with
the Tiber and Castel
Sant'Angelo*
vellum, inv. 1890 no. 1247
signed and dated 1685

This scene of a bend in the
River Tiber is full of light,
highlighting every detail; it
is dominated on the right,
on the opposite bank, by
Castel Sant'Angelo, St. Peter's Basilica and the Vatican Palaces. This painting's
counterpart is on display at
II-28 and it is probably that
Vittoria della Rovere bought
the two works, signed and
dated 1685, during the artist's first visit to Florence
in 1690.

II-9
Eglon Hendrik
van der Neer
*Landscape with
Herdsmen*
wood panel, inv. 1890
no. 1213
1696–1697
doc. in 1715
GPF. M (1713)

II-10
Christoph Ludwig
Agricola
*Landscape with
Herdsmen and Cattle*
copper, inv. 1890 no. 1137
GPF. M (1713)

II-11
Caspar van Wittel
*View of the Tiber with
the Church of San
Giovanni dei Fiorentini*
vellum, inv. 1890 no. 4354
1685
In this scene the Church of
San Giovanni dei Fiorentini
stands out on the right and
the bridge and the Castel
Sant'Angelo can be seen in
the background. The painting's counterpart is also on
display here (II-25) and
both works are dated 1685;
the artist probably brought
the paintings to Florence
when he came to the city
for the second time in 1694.

II-12
Jan Frans van Bredael (?)
*Landscape with
Paesants returning
from a Fair*
wood panel, inv. OdA
1911 no. 72
initialled: Johann Frans
Bredael

II-13
Jan de Momper (?)
River Landscape

canvas, inv. 1890 no. 6205
signed: Momper
doc. in 1773
GPF. M

II-14
Jan van Kessel and
Erasmus II Quellin
Allegory of Sight
copper, inv. 1890 no. 1216
signed and dated 1664
doc. at Palazzo Pitti in
1828
C III. M (1667)

II-15
Paul Bril
*Landscape
with a Hare Hunt*
copper, inv. 1890 no. 1136
c. 1595
signed
doc. in 1772

II-16
Adriaen Frans
Baudewijns and
Pieter Bout
*River Landscape
with a Church*
canvas, inv. 1890 no. 1227
signed: Both e Baudouin
doc. in 1796

II-17
Jan Brueghel the Elder
*Orpheus in the
Underworld*
copper, inv. 1890 no. 1298
signed and dated 1594
doc. in 1704

19	23	26	29	32
20	24	27	30	33
21				
22	25	28	31	34

II-8

II-11

II-18
Frans Francken II
Crucifixion
copper, inv. 1890 no. 1121
doc. at Palazzo Pitti in
1666

II-19
Jan Frans
van Bredael (?)
*River Landscape with
Cattle*
wood panel, inv. OdA
1911 no. 73

II-20
Jan de Momper (?)
*Landscape with a
Herdsman and his
Cattle*
canvas, inv. 1890 no. 1054
doc. in 1881

II-21
Jan van Kessel and
Erasmus II Quellin
Allegory of Taste
copper, inv. 1890 no. 1199
doc. at Palazzo Pitti in
1828
C III. M (1667)

II-22
Paul Bril
*Landscape
with a Stag Hunt*
copper, inv. 1890 no. 1129
signed and dated 1595
doc. in 1772
C II. M (1635)

II-23
Eglon Hendrik
van der Neer
*Landscape with
Washerwomen*
wood panel, inv. 1890
no. 1205
doc. in 1715
GPF. M (1713)

II-24
Christoph Ludwig
Agricola
*Landscape with a
Rainbow*
copper, inv. 1890 no. 1130
GPF. M (1713)

II-25
Caspar van Wittel
*View of Campus
Martius from the Prati
di Castello*
vellum, inv. 1890 no. 4355
1685

II-26
Lodewijk de Vadder (?)
*Landscape with Figures
in a Wood*
canvas, inv. 1912, no. 459

II-27
Anastagio Fontebuoni
*St. John the Baptist
Preaching*
copper, inv. 1912 no. 366
doc. in 1828
C II. M

II-28
Caspar van Wittel
*View of the Villa Medici
in Rome*
vellum, inv. 1890 no. 1256
signed and dated 1685
doc. in 1691

II-29
Moyses van
Uyttenbroeck
*Landscape with Ruins
and Herdsmen*
wood panel, inv. 1890
no. 1265
1624
doc. in 1784
GPF. M

II-30
Filippo Napoletano (?)
*Landscape with Christ
and the Cananite
Woman*
copper, inv. 1890 no. 1266
doc. at Palazzo Pitti in 1774

II-31
Pieter de Molijn
*Landscape with a
Bridge*
wood panel, inv. 1890
no. 1290
c. 1656
signed
doc. at Palazzo Pitti in
1715

II-32
Abraham van
Diepenbeeck
*Madonna of the
Apocalypse*
canvas, inv. 1890 no. 1105
c. 1645
doc. in 1793

II-33
Pietro Mera
*Pan, Syrinx and
Nymphs*
copper, inv. 1890 no. 1147
signed
doc. at Palazzo Pitti in
1774

II-34
Mathys Schoevaerts
*Landscape with a
Village*
wood panel, inv. 1890
no. 1112
signed

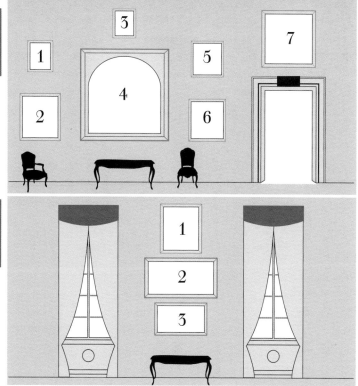

Justice Room (Sala della Giustizia)

In Medici times this room was part of a utility area next to the Grand Ducal apartments. Between 1770 and 1776 it was occupied, along with the rooms around it, by Maria Anna, the daughter of Grand Duke Peter Leopold of Hapsburg Lorraine. According to an 1813 plan of Palazzo Pitti it was called the "salon de famille" and preceded a large dining room, now the Flora and Putti Rooms.

After the return of Grand Duke Ferdinand II of Hapsburg Lorraine the ceiling was decorated in 1819-1820 by Antonio Fedi with an allegory of *Justice* accompanied by Mercury, alluding to the trade and prosperity assured by the return of the sovereign.

Wall I

I-1
Pietro Vecchia
Portrait of a Woman
canvas, inv. 1912 no. 222
L. M (1675)

I-2
Paolo Veronese
Portrait of a Man
canvas, inv. 1912 no. 108
c. 1570–1580
L. M (1659)

I-5
French school,
17th century
Portrait of a Man
canvas, inv. 1912 no. 126
(inv. 1890 no. 8431)
doc. at Palazzo Pitti in
1819

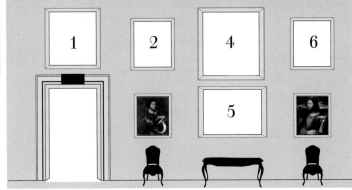

I-4
Bonifacio Veronese
*Christ among the
Doctors*
canvas, inv. 1912 no. 405
doc. in 1816

I-5
Venetian school (?),
16th century
*Portrait of Costanza
Bentivoglio*
canvas, inv. 1912 no. 221
dated 1520
doc. in 1688; doc. at
Palazzo Pitti in 1828

I-6
Garofalo
St. James Major
canvas, inv. 1912 no. 5
L. M (1675)

I-7
Titian's school
*Portrait of Cosimo
Bartoli*
canvas, inv. 1912 no. 389
doc. in 1706
GPF. M

Wall II

II-1
Tintoretto's school
Portrait of a Man
canvas, inv. 1912 no. 339
L. M (1675)

II-2
Leandro Bassano
Last Supper
canvas, inv. 1912 no. 446

c. 1590
V. DR (1631); GPF. M
(1713)

II-3
Giovanni Demio
*Rest on the Flight into
Egypt*
canvas, inv. 1890 no. 6069
c. 1558
GPF. M (1713)

Wall III

III-1
Domenico Tintoretto
Portrait of a Man
canvas, inv.1912 no. 410
GPF . M (1713)

III-2
Domenico Tintoretto (?)
Portrait of a Man
canvas, inv. 1912, no. 65
doc. At Palazzo Pitti from
1834

III-3
Titian
*Portrait of a Man
(Tommaso Mosti)*
canvas, inv. 1912 no. 495
L. M (1663-1667)

This portrait has been identified as a man from Ferrara
called Tommaso Mosti on
uncertain grounds based
on an old but not coeval
inscription on the back of
the original canvas which
identifies Titian as the artist and 1526 as the year of
execution. It was bought by

Cardinal Leopold de' Medici as a work by Titian and
appears in the 1665–1667
inventory of his collec-
tions. It was downgraded
as a copy in 1675 but is
now unanimously believed
to be one of the maestro's
masterpieces in which his
capacity for psychological
introspection meets with
his magnificent portrayal
of the fur-lined cloak.

III-4
after Titian
copy of the *Portrait of
Alfonso I d'Este*
canvas, inv. 1912 no. 311
doc. at Palazzo Pitti in 1798

III-5
Bonifacio Veronese
*Emperor Augustus and
the Sibyl*
canvas, inv. 1912 no. 257
L. M (1675)

III-6
Bassano family circle
Portrait of a Woman
canvas, inv. 1912 no. 130
doc. at Palazzo Pitti in
1819

III-7
Titian
Christ the Saviour
wood panel, inv. 1912
no. 228
V. DR (1631)

Like many others in Pal-
azzo Pitti and the Uffizi Gallery, this painting came to

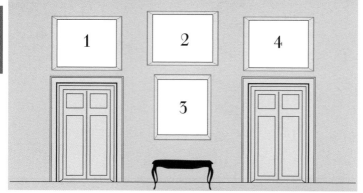

Florence in 1631 as part of the inheritance of Vittoria della Rovere, the last descendent of the Dukes of Urbino and the wife of Grand Duke Ferdinando II de' Medici. Commissioned by Duke Francesco Maria della Rovere, perhaps for his consort Eleonora Gonzaga before the 7th July 1532, it was completed two years later by Titian. The Saviour is depicted with great expressive intensity and stands out against the landscape, which fades away into the distance amidst the vivid hues of twilight.

Wall IV

IV-1
Bonifacio Veronese
Rest on the Flight into Egypt
wood panel, inv. 1912 no. 89
c. 1620–1630
GPF. M (1713)

IV-2
Titian's studio
Madonna and Child, St. Catherine of Alexandria and the Young St. John
canvas, inv. 1912 no. 17
doc. in 1624
GPF. M (1694)

IV-3
Titian's studio
Portrait of a Gentleman

III-3

canvas, inv. 1912 no. 494
GPF. M (1713)

IV-4
Venetian school, 16th century
Holy Family with the Young St. John and St. Elizabeth
wood panel, inv. 1912 no. 254
GPF. M (1713)

III-7

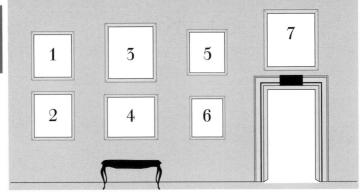

Flora Room (Sala di Flora)

In Medici times this room, like those around it, was part of a utility area for the Grand Ducal apartments. From around 1770 to 1776 it was used by Maria Anna, daughter of Grand Duke Peter Leopold of Hapsburg Lorraine. The plans for this area of the building, prepared by Elisa Baciocchi during the Napoleonic era, combined this room with the Putti Room to create a large dining area. After Grand Duke Ferdinand II's return from exile, the ceiling was decorated between 1810 and 1820 with an allegory of *Flora* by Antonio Marini.

Wall I

I-1
Alessandro Allori (?)
Portrait of Isabella de' Medici (?)
wood panel, inv. 1890 no. 8738
doc. at Palazzo Pitti in 1828

I-2
Michele di Ridolfo del Ghirlandaio
Portrait of a Woman
wood panel, inv. 1912 no. 28
c. 1560–1570
doc. at Palazzo Pitti in 1828

I-3
Michele di Ridolfo del Ghirlandaio
Holy Family
wood panel, inv. 1912 no. 180
c. 1560–1570
doc. in 1777

I-4
Friedrich Sustris
Birth of a Child
canvas, inv. 1912 no. 394
c. 1565
doc. in 1589

I-5
Bonifacio Veronese
Holy Family
canvas, inv. 1890 no. 3349
doc. in 1906; doc. at Palazzo Pitti in 1928

I-6
Cigoli
Holy Family
wood panel, inv. 1912 no. 239
c. 1585
doc. at Palazzo Pitti in 1704
M. M (1669)

I-7
Giorgio Vasari
Holy Family with St. Elizabeth and the Young St. John
wood panel, inv. 1912 no. 413
c. 1550
doc. at Palazzo Pitti in 1819

Wall II

II-1
Adriaen Thomas Key
Portrait of a Man
wood panel, inv. 1912 no. 7

II-2
Alessandro Allori
Madonna and Child
canvas, inv. 1912 no. 442
The origin of this painting and the date it came into Palazzo Pitti's collections are unknown. The work is noteworthy for both its Bronzino-esque grace and the intimate and familiar tone of the portrayal, in line with the principles of the Counter-Reformation. It was done during the 1580s at the time of Grand Duke Ferdinando I, who was a Cardinal of the Holy Roman Church until he

married Christine of Lorraine in 1589.

II-3
Florentine school,
17th century
Portrait of a Cook
canvas, inv. 1912 no. 435
F III. AL (1822)

II-4
Titian
*Adoration of the
Shepherds*
wood panel, inv. 1912 no. 423
1532
V. DR (1631)
GPF. M

II-5
Giorgio Vasari
Oration in the Garden
wood panel, inv. 1912
no. 385
c. 1560
doc. at Palazzo Pitti in 1828

Wall III

III-1
Benedetto Gennari
copy of the *David* by
Guercino
canvas, inv. 1912 no. 143
F III. AL (1818)

III-2
Domenico Puligo
*Madonna and Child
with St. John the
Baptist*
wood panel, inv. 1912 no. 145
c. 1525

doc. at Palazzo Pitti from 1791
C. M (1666)

III-3
Domenico Puligo
Portrait of a Man
wood panel, inv. 1912 no. 184
c. 1525
doc. in 1638
GPF. M (1710)

III-4
Domenico Puligo
*Madonna and Child,
Young St. John and
St. Lawrence*
wood panel, inv. 1912 no. 146
c. 1515
doc. at Palazzo Pitti
in 1829

II-2

77

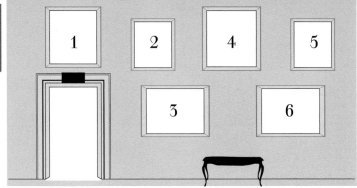

III-5
Francesco and Jacopo
Bassano's studio
Autumn
canvas, inv. 1912 no. 383
c. 1580–1590

III-6
Jacopo and Francesco
Bassano
*God speaks to Noah
after the Flood*
canvas, inv. 1912 no. 386
c. 1578
F I. M. (1578)

Wall IV

IV-1
Carl Ruthart
*Stag attacked by Wild
Animals*
canvas, inv. 1912 no. 438
c. 1670
C III. M (1676)

IV-2
Carletto Caliari
*St. Catherine of
Alexandria at Prayer*
inv. 1890 no. 890
doc. in 1796; doc. at Pal-
azzo Pitti in 1928
L. M. (1675)

IV-3
Perugino
St. Mary Magdalene
wood panel, inv. 1912
no. 42
V. DR; L. M (1675)
doc. in 1641
The saint, wearing elegant
clothes, can be identified
by the inscription in gold
letters on the edge of the
cloak. The work can be dated to the 1490s and conveys
a befitting sense of grace,
showing the influence of
Flemish painting. It is a
work of the maturity of the
Umbrian artist, who lived
and worked in Florence.
The origin of the piece is
unknown and it was docu-
mented for the first time in
1641 in possession of Vittoria della Rovere in the Villa
of Poggio Imperiale.

IV-4
Melchior de
Hondecoeter
Farmyard Foul
canvas, inv. 1912 no. 400
(1890 no. 8434)
signed
doc. in 1823

IV-5
Anton van Dyck
*Rest on the Flight
into Egypt*
canvas, inv. 1912 no. 437
FIII. AL (1818)
Another version of this
work hangs in the Hermit-
age Museum and there are
numerous copies done by
other artists from the time,
attesting to its popularity. It
was part of the Gerini Collection and was bought by
Ferdinand II of Hapsburg
Lorraine in 1818 to join Palazzo Pitti's Gallery. It was
commonly believed to be a
copy of the Russian version,
but thanks to a restoration
in 1999 which revealed
its pictorial quality, it is
now considered to be the
work of the artist himself
and can be traced back to
his English period. The
involvement of the artist's
studio has been identified
as limited to the depiction
of the angels in the top right
of the composition.

IV-6
Carl Ruthart
*Wild Animals in a
Wood*
canvas, inv. 1912 no. 418
c. 1670
signed
C III. M (1676)

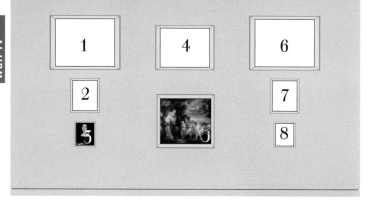

IV-7
Domenico Puligo
Holy Family
wood panel, inv. 1912
no. 486
c. 1515
doc. at Palazzo Pitti in
1761

IV-8
Lo Spagna
*Mystical Marriage
of St. Catherine of
Alexandra, St. Anthony
of Padua and
St. Francis*
wood panel, inv. 1912
no. 499
c. 1520
doc. in 1859

IV-3

IV-5

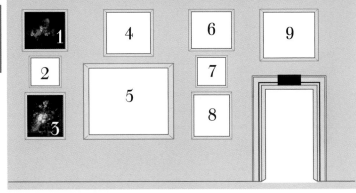

Putti Room (Sala dei Putti)

In Medici times this room was one of the utility areas next to the Grand Ducal apartments, although from 1770 to 1776 it became part of the suite of rooms used by Maria Anna, the daughter of Grand Duke Peter Leopold of Hapsburg Lorraine. During the Napoleonic era (1813) an adjoining wall onto the Flora Room was removed to create a large dining area, but after the return of Grand Duke Ferdinand II of Lorraine it was separated off once again and the room was reserved predominantly for Flemish and Dutch paintings from the seventeenth century. The ceiling decoration with three flying putti (cherubs), which give the room its name, is the work of Antonio Marini and can be dated to around 1830.

Wall I

I-1
Willem van Aelst
Still Life with Fruit, Parrot and Nautilus Pitcher
canvas, inv. 1912 no. 468
signed and dated 1653
L. M

This painting is one of a pair by the same artist with the same subject in this room (inv. 1912 no. 469, see I-6), both signed and dated "W.V.Aelst 1653". These still life compositions are two of nine works by the refined Dutch artist which excited the preference and appreciation of the Medici family in the seventeenth century. In the second of these two works, the presence of a nautilus pitcher (now in the Museo degli Argenti) leads us to suppose that

it was done in Florence, commissioned by Cardinal Leopoldo de' Medici.

I-2
Eglon Hendrik van der Neer
Esther faints before Ahasuerus
canvas, inv. 1890 no. 1186
signed and dated 1696
doc. in 1697
C III. M

I-3
Rachel Ruysch
Flowers in a Vase with Pomegranates
canvas inv. 1912 no. 455
1716
FIII. AL

This painting, along with the *Still Life with Fruit, Flowers, Reptiles and Insects* in the same room (see I-8) is signed and dated "Rachel Ruysch 1716". Formerly in

the Wattier collection in Paris, this work was acquired for Palazzo Pitti in 1823 by Grand Duke Ferdinand II of Hapsburg Lorraine. The Dutch painter distinguishes herself for her virtuosity in the pictorial representation of the smallest details of the plants and flowers, a characteristic which made her highly regarded all over Europe.

I-4
Bartolomeo Schedoni (?)
copy of the *Assumption of the Virgin* by **Annibale Carracci**
canvas, inv. 1912 no. 231
doc. at Palazzo Pitti in 1687

I-5
Salvator Rosa
Peace burning the Arms of War

I-1

canvas, inv. 1912 no. 453
signed
GC. M (1663)

I-6
Willem van Aelst
Still Life with Fruit and Precious Vases
canvas, inv. 1912 no. 469
L. M
signed and dated 1653
See I-1.

I-7
Willem van Aelst
Still Life with Fruit
canvas, inv. OdA 1911
no. 498
c. 1652
doc. in 1669
GC. M (1663)

I-8
Rachel Ruysch
Still Life with Fruit, Flowers, Reptiles and Insects
canvas, inv. 1912 no. 451
doc. in 1823
FIII. AL
See I-3.

I-3

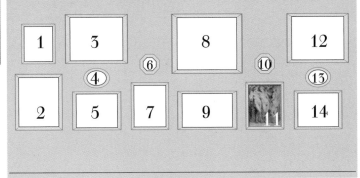

I-9
Dutch school,
18th century
Boar-Hunting Scene
canvas, inv. 1890 no. 1304
doc. in 1796

III-1
Otto Marseus van
Schrieck
*Butterflies, Snake and
a Thistle*
canvas, inv. OdA 1911
no. 501
1668
C III. M

III-2
Pieter van Laer
A Country Stable
canvas, inv. 1890 no. 1222
doc. at Palazzo Pitti in
1798

III-3
Paul Bril
Landscape with Herds
canvas, inv. 1912 no. 449
C. M (1618)

III-4
Herman van Swanevelt
*Landscape with
Travellers*
copper, inv. 1890 no. 2142

III-5
Jacob van Ruisdael
*Landscape with a
Waterfall*

canvas, inv. 1912 no. 429
(inv. 1890 no. 8436)
signed
doc. at Palazzo Pitti in
1834
L II. AL (1827)

III-6
Michelangelo
Cerquozzi
Wool Carder
slate, inv. 1890 no. 1250
doc. in 1753

III-7
Herman van Swanevelt
(?)
*Landscape with
Travellers at an Inn*
canvas, inv. 1912 no. 412
doc. in 1698; doc. at Palazzo Pitti in 1828

III-8
Godfried Schalcken
*Young Girl holding a
Candle*
canvas, inv. 1890 no. 1118
signed
doc. in 1698; doc. at
Palazzo Pitti in 1928

III-9
Jacob Jordaens
*Neptune creating the
Horse*
canvas, inv. 1890 no. 1234
c. 1644
signed
doc. at Palazzo Pitti in
1728

III-10
Michelangelo
Cerquozzi
Shepherd with a Dog
slate, inv. 1890 no. 1252
doc. in 1753

III-11
Peter Paul Rubens
The Three Graces
wood panel, inv. 1890
no. 1165
L. M (1671)

This panting was done by
the famous Flemish painter
around 1622 and depicts the
three Graces, Aglaia (Beau-
ty), Euphrosyne (Mirth)
and Thalia (Good Cheer).
It was given by Monsignor
Airoldi, apostolic nuncio
in Brussels, to Cardinal
Leopoldo de' Medici in
1671. This type of painting
can be classified as "small-
scale" work, constituted in
general by sketches and
designs for paintings of
a larger size; these small
works of art are notable for
their use of pure, essential
forms and colour, and their
pictorial immediacy.

III-12
Paul Bril
*Landscape with the
Return of the Herds*
canvas, inv. 1912 no. 452
C. M (1618)

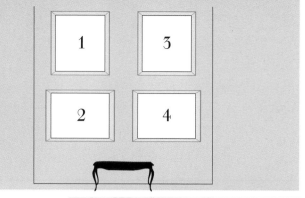

III-13
Herman van Swanevelt
Landscape with Fishermen
copper, inv. 1890 no. 2143

III-14
Jérome Galle
Still Life with a Festoon of Flowers
canvas, inv. 1890 no. 1268
signed and dated 1655
doc. in 1753; doc. at
Palazzo Pitti in 1928

Wall IV

IV-1
Willem van Aelst
Still Life with a Goat's Head
canvas, inv. 1912 no. 454
signed and dated 1652
GC. M

IV-2
Ludolf Bakhuysen
Seascape with Sailing Ships
canvas, inv. 1912 no. 464
dated 1669, initialled: LB
F III. AL (1823)

IV-3
Willem van Aelst
Still Life with Game
canvas, inv. 1912 no. 466
signed and dated 1652
GC. M

III-11

IV-4
Hendrick Jacobsz
Dubbels
Seascape with a View of the Coast at Texel
canvas, inv. 1912 no. 457
c. 1653–1655
signed
L II. AL (1834)

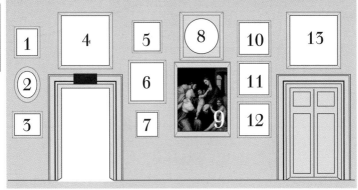

Ulysses Room (Sala di Ulisse)

In Medici times this room was used as the Grand Duke's bedchamber, though when the Hapsburg Lorraine family came to power it was inhabited around 1775 by Maria Theresa, Peter Leopold's oldest daughter. When Grand Duke Ferdinand II returned from exile in 1815, Gasparo Martellini decorated the ceiling with the *Return of Ulysses to Ithaca* and a frieze with *Fidelity*, *Fortitude*, *Hercules* and *Apollo*, subjects alluding to the return of the sovereign to his State after the Napoleonic period.

Wall I

I-1
Tintoretto's studio
Portrait of a Man
canvas, inv. 1912 no. 330
late 16th century
L. M. (1675)

I-2
Francesco Furini
Faith
canvas, inv. 1912 no. 428
c. 1633–1640
doc. at Palazzo Pitti in 1859

I-3
Agostino Carracci
Landscape with Bathers
canvas, inv. 1912 no. 320
signed: DI MANO DI AGOSTINO CARRACCI
doc. in 1677
F III. AL (1818)

I-4
Salvator Rosa
Temptations of St. Anthony Abbot
canvas, inv. 1912 no. 297
c. 1645
GC. M

I-5
Bernardino Licinio
Portrait of a Man
canvas, inv. 1912 no. 69
1537

I-6
Carlo Dolci
Portrait of Claudia Felicita as Galla Placidia
canvas, inv. 1890 no. 2148
dated 1675, signed: ... da me Carlo Dolci...
C III. M

I-7
Cristofano Allori
Portrait of a Man
tempera on flat roof tile, inv. 1912 no. 497
c. 1605
L. M

I-8
Guido Reni
Charity
canvas, inv. 1912 no. 197
c. 1605
L. M (1675)

I-9
Raphael
Madonna and Child, Young St. John and two Saints (Madonna of the Cloth)
wood panel, inv. 1912 no. 127
C I. M; GPF. M (1697)

This painting on wood was done around 1514 for the rich banker Bindo Altoviti, though after the buyer sided against Cosimo I de' Medici, it was confiscated and came into the Duke's collection in the mid-sixteenth century. It depicts the Baby Jesus being passed to the Virgin Mary by an elderly saint (Elizabeth or Anne) as the Young St. John points to the scene and the Baby turns towards a young saint (Catherine?).

Wall II

1		4		8
2				9
3	5	6	7	10

This work takes it name from the window in the background, which is covered by oiled cloths in a manner consistent with customs of the time.

I-10
Anthonis Mor's school
Portrait of a Woman
wood panel, inv. 1890 no. 1841
late 16th century
signed and dated 1579

I-11
Giulio Campi
Portrait of a Man
wood panel, inv. 1912 no. 493
c. 1525–1530
doc. at Palazzo Pitti in 1828

I-12
Tintoretto (?)
Portrait of a Clergyman
canvas, inv. 1912 no. 74
doc. in 1662
L. M (1675)

I-13
Giorgio Vasari
Temptations of St. Jerome
wood panel, inv. 1912 no. 393
1541
doc. in 1541
O. M

Wall II

II-1
Cristofano Allori
St. John the Baptist in the Desert

canvas, inv. 1912 no. 305
c. 1612–1615
C. M (1666)

II-2
Giovan Battista Moroni
Portrait of Simone di Marco Moroni
canvas, inv. 1912 no. 121
c. 1570
doc. at Palazzo Pitti from 1798
L. M (1668)

II-3
Pietro Ciafferi
Christ led away from the Praetorium
canvas, inv. 1912 no. 448
initialled: PC

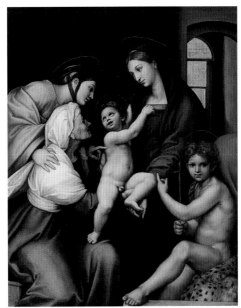

I-9

II-4
Andrea del Sarto
*Madonna and Child
in Glory with Saints
(Gambassi Altarpiece)*
wood panel, inv. 1912
no. 307
doc. in 1637

This work was probably
painted as an *ex voto* for
the plague of 1527–1528. It
depicts the Virgin Mary and
her Son in glory with St. John
the Baptist, St. Roch, St. Sebastian, St. Mary Magdalene,
St. Onophrius and St. Lawrence, the final two being the
titular saints of the church of
the hermit nuns of Gambassi
in Tuscany, the birth place
of the buyer, Domenico da
Gambassi known as Becuc-
cio; Becuccio was a 'bicchi-
eraio' (glass maker/seller)
and a friend of the artist. The
painting is documented as
being part of the Medicean
collections in 1637 at the
time of Grand Duke Ferdi-
nando II de' Medici.

II-5
Agostino Tassi
Diana and Actaeon
canvas, inv. 1912 no. 474
c. 1640

II-6
Filippino Lippi
Stories of Lucretia
wood panel, inv. 1912 no. 388
This painting, like the *Stories of Virginia* in the Louvre Museum, adorned the
front of a wedding chest;
both works are exactly the
same size and came from the
same wooden casing. Here
we can see three episodes
from Lucretia's life: her body
is brought out by her family after she has committed
suicide following her rape by
Sextus Tarquinius; the Roman people lament over her
body; and the people rebel
against King Tarquinius Su-
perbus, Sextus' father. It is
still a juvenile work, dated to
the 1470s, showing influence
from Botticelli but it already
reveals the artist's own agi-
tated and capricious style.

II-7
after Annibale Carracci
copy of the *Nymph
with Satyr*
paper affixed to a wood
panel, inv. 1912 no. 480

17th century
L. M (1675)

II-8
Orazio Riminaldi
Love Victorious
canvas, inv. 1912 no. 422
c. 1624
doc. at Pitti at the end of
the 17th century

II-9
Giovan Battista Moroni
Portrait of a Woman
canvas, inv. 1912 no. 128
c. 1560
doc. at Palazzo Pitti in 1695
L. M. (1665)

II-10
Alessandro Allori
*Sermon of St. John
the Baptist*

II-

II-6

copper, inv. 1912 no. 291
1604
signed
doc. in 1604; doc. at
Palazzo Pitti in 1666

Wall III

III-1
Carlo Dolci's school
St. Lucy
canvas, inv. 1912 no. 295
17th century
doc. at Palazzo Pitti in
1834

III-2
Bartolomeo Schedoni
St. Paul
wood panel, inv. 1912 no. 333
c. 1610
L. M (1675)

III-3
Domenico Puligo's studio
Holy Family
wood panel, inv. 1912 no. 294
1520s
doc. at Palazzo Pitti in 1773

III-4
School of Bergamo,
16th century
Portrait of a Man
canvas, inv. 1912 no. 120
doc. at Palazzo Pitti in 1761
L. M (1668)

III-5
Carlo Dolci
Madonna and Child
canvas, inv. 1912 no. 302
c. 1680

doc. at Palazzo Pitti in 1723
V. DR

III-6
Carlo Dolci
*Vision of St. John the
Evangelist on Patmos*
copper, inv. 1912 no. 465
c. 1550 (?)
signed: Carlino Dolci
V. DR (1694)

III-7
Francesco Curradi
*St. Catherine of
Alexandria*
canvas, inv. 1912 no. 286

III-8
Cristofano Allori
Dinner at Emmaus
canvas, inv. 1912 no. 303
c. 1610
C. M (1666)

III-9
Carlo Dolci
Ecce Homo
canvas, inv. 1912 no. 321
c. 1670
doc. at Palazzo Pitti in 1687
C. M (1666)

III-10
Giovan Battista Moroni
*Portrait of Prelate
Marco di Giovanni
Moroni*
canvas, inv. 1912 no. 127
c. 1570
doc. at Palazzo Pitti in 1798
L. M (1668)

III-11
Tintoretto
*Madonna and Child
(Madonna of the
Conception)*
canvas, inv. 1912 no. 313
c. 1570
L. M (1658)

III-12
Gregorio Pagani
Portrait of a Man
canvas, inv. 1912 no. 285
c. 1600
L. M (1675)

III-13
Florentine school,
17th century
Portrait of a Young Man
canvas, inv. 1912 no. 402

III-14
Tintoretto
*Portrait of Andrea
Frizier*
canvas, inv. 1912 no. 70
c. 1575
L. M (1675)

III-15
Venetian school (?),
16th century
*Portrait of Bishop
Giuliano Argentino*
canvas, inv. 1912 no. 35
c. 1537–1549
doc. at Palazzo Pitti in
1687–1688
L. M; GC. M (1654)

III-16
Cigoli
Ecce Homo
canvas, inv. 1912 no. 90
1607
DL. M (1630)
This painting has great realistic and dramatic impact and was done in 1607 for the Roman patrician Massimo Massimi who, two years previously, had commissioned a painting with the same subject from Caravaggio. Cigoli excelled in this challenge and met with great success both in Rome and in Florence, where the work could be found in 1630 in possession of Don Lorenzo de' Medici. Eight years later, it was documented as being in Grand Duke Ferdinando de' Medici's bedchamber, a position which proved its popularity.

III-17
Hans von Aachen
Self Portrait
canvas, inv. 1912 no. 329
c. 1585–1595

III-18
Frans Pourbus the Younger
Portrait of a Man
canvas, inv. 1912 no. 296
c. 1595 (?)
doc. at Palazzo Pitti in 1834

III-19
Antonio del Ceraiolo (?)
Portrait of a Man
wood panel, inv. 1912 no. 491
c. 1520–1550
doc. at Palazzo Pitti in 1687
L. M (1675)

Napoleon's Bathroom (Bagno di Napoleone)

This room is part of the area Giuseppe Cacialli renovated in 1813, converting it into Emperor Napoleon's apartment by order of his sister Elisa Baciocchi, Grand Duchess of Tuscany from 1808 to 1814.

The stuccoes by Luigi Pampaloni in the lunettes depict scenes inspired by ancient mythology.

The niches hold four marble statues of Nereids in a neoclassical style, like the room around them. Two of the statues are the work of Salvatore Bongiovanni and the others are by Giovanni Insom.

Education of Jupiter Room (Sala dell'Educazione di Giove)

In Medici times the Grand Duke's secretary used this room and it continued to be part of the Grand Ducal apartments even in the Lorraine era until it joined the Palatine Gallery. The ceiling was decorated by Luigi Catani in 1819 and depicts Jupiter as a young boy. He is taken away from his father Chronus, who would have eaten him like his brothers, and hidden by his mother Rhea on the island of Crete, where he was brought up by the nymph Adrastea and suckled by the goat Amalthea. The hexagons hold images of *Cybele*, *Neptune* and *Amphitrite*, *Juno* and *Mars*.

Wall I

I-1
Giovanni Bilivert (?)
St. Sebastian
canvas, inv. 1912 no. 271
GPF. M (1713)

I-2
Justus Suttermans
Portrait of Vittoria della Rovere and Cosimo III as a *Holy Family*
canvas, inv. 1912 no. 232
c. 1645
FM. M

I-3
Carlo Dolci
St. Domenic Penitent
canvas, inv. 1912 no. 406
1645–1646
C. M (1666)

I-4
Cristofano Allori
Judith with the Head of Holofernes
canvas, inv. 1912 no. 96
FII. M; C. M

I-4

This painting was in the artist's studio when he died in 1621 and must have been completed a short time previously. It then came directly into the Medicean collections, given by Grand Duke Ferdinando II to his uncle Cardinal Carlo. When the Cardinal died in 1666 it came back into the possession of the Grand Duke. According to historical sources, the artist is thought to have painted himself as Holofernes, while he gave the biblical heroine the appearance of Maria di Giovanni Mazzafirri (known as "La Mazzafirra"), his lover, and the maidservant the features of the lady's mother. This is the artist's most famous work and there are several known original copies.

I-5
Francesco Salviati
Lamentation over the Dead Christ
wood panel, inv. 1912 no. 115
c. 1545
doc. in 1591
doc. Medici collections
doc. at Palazzo Pitti in 1828

I-6
Carlo Dolci
Martyrdom of St. Andrew
canvas, inv. 1912 no. 266
FIII. AL (1818)
This painting, signed and dated "1646 CAROLUS DOLCIUS FAC. T", depicts the crucifixion of St. Andrew Apostle, St. Peter's brother, and was painted for the Florentine Marquis Carlo Gerini. It was copied at least twice and is the artist's most famous work. Dolci painted many religious works which were extremely popular in seventeenth-century Florence, particularly with the Medici

family. In 1818 Grand Duke Ferdinand II of Lorraine bought the painting for his collection.

I-7
after Guercino
copy of *Susanna and the Elders*
canvas, inv. 1912 no. 234
doc. at Palazzo Pitti in 1761

I-8
after Correggio
copy of *Ecce Homo*
copper, inv. 1912 no. 259

I-9
Veronese's school, 16th century
Portrait of a Child
canvas, inv. 1912 no. 267
GC. M

I-10
Veronese's school, 16th century
Portrait of a Child
canvas, inv. 1912 no. 268
GC. M

I-11
Scipione Pulzone
Portrait of Ferdinando I de' Medici
copper, inv. 1912 no. 337
post 1590
L. M (1675)

I-12
François Clouet's studio
Portrait of Henry II of France
wood panel, inv. 1912 no. 262
C. L.

I-13
Filippo Napoletano
The Snail Vendor
copper, inv. 1890 no. 1009
doc. at Palazzo Pitti in 1769

II-1
Veronese's studio, 16th century
Resurrection
canvas, inv. 1912 no. 264
doc. at Palazzo Pitti in 1694
MM. A (1624)

II-2
Jan Anthonisz van Ravesteyn
Portrait of Daniel Heinsius
canvas, inv. 1912 no. 255
signed and dated 1629
GPF. M

II-3
Giovanni Bonconsiglio
Madonna and Child, St. James and St. Catherine of Alexandria (?)
wood panel, inv. 1912 no. 338
c. 1515–1520

II-4
Tintoretto's studio
Deposition from the Cross
canvas, inv. 1912 no. 248
GPF. M (1698)

II-5
Anton van Dyck
Portrait of a Man
canvas, inv. 1912 no. 258
c. 1638
doc. in 1704; doc. at Palazzo Pitti in 1780

I-6

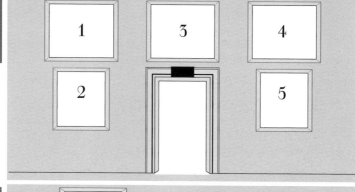

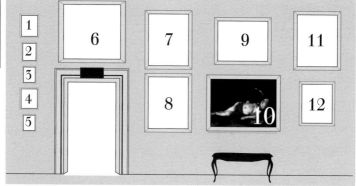

III-1
Francesco Maria Bassi
Head of an Old Man
wood panel, inv. 1912 no. 308
doc. at Palazzo Pitti in 1761

III-2
Giovanni Bilivert
St. Catherine of Alexandria
slate, inv. 1890 no. 1402
c. 1638

III-3
Follower of Bronzino
Portrait of Giovanni de' Medici (?)
wood panel, inv. 1912 no. 279

III-4
Jean Clouet
Portrait of Claude of Lorraine, Duke of Guise
wood panel, inv. 1912 no. 252
c. 1525–1530
C. L (1589)

III-5
Bronzino's studio
Portrait of Lucrezia de' Medici
tin, inv. 1912 no. 277
c. 1560

III-6
Alessandro Maganza
Herod's Banquet
canvas, inv. 1912 no. 387
V. DR (1691)

III-7
after Anton van Dyck
copy of the *Portrait of Henrietta Maria of England*
canvas, inv. 1912 no. 331
doc. at Palazzo Pitti in 1824
V. DR (1691)

III-8
Benedetto Caliari
Apparition of Christ to the Holy Women
canvas, inv. 1912 no. 134
C III. M

III-9
Venetian school,
16th century
Rest during the flight to Egypt
canvas, inv. 1890 no. 607
FM. M (1685)

III-10
Caravaggio
Sleeping Cupid
canvas, inv. 1912 no. 183
1608
L. M (1667)
This painting is one of Caravaggio's late works. It was painted on Malta in 1608 for Francesco dell'Antella,

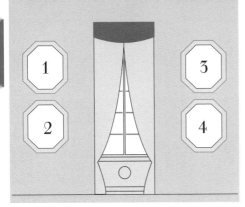

commander of the Order of St. John (the Knights of Malta), who had it reproduced in 1619 by Giovanni da San Giovanni in a fresco on the façade of his house in Piazza Santa Croce. The classical theme of the sleeping cupid is rendered here with intense realism and a preponderance of dark and light tones with few intermediate shades. In 1667 it came into the collection of Prince Cardinal Leopoldo de' Medici in Palazzo Pitti, who had it fitted with its splendid frame adorned with the attributes of the quiver and the arrows.

III-11
Veronese's school
16th century
Portrait of an Artist
canvas, inv. 1912 no. 68
c. 1550–1555

III-12
Benedetto Caliari
Christ bidding his Mother Farewell
canvas, inv. 1912 no. 136
C III. M

IV-1
Bartolomeo Mancini
St. Henry of Bavaria and St. Cunigunde
canvas, inv. 1912 no. 276
dated 1689, signed: B°
Mancini F
C III. M

IV-2
Carlo Dolci
St. Charles Borromeo
canvas, inv. 1912 no. 275
1656–1660
C. M (1666)

IV-3
Bartolomeo Mancini
St. Francis Saverio
canvas, inv. 1912 no. 280
dated 1687, signed: Bartolomeo Mancini F
C III. M

IV-4
Carlo Dolci
St. Nicholas of Tolentino
canvas, inv. 1912 no. 281
1656–1661
C. M (1666)

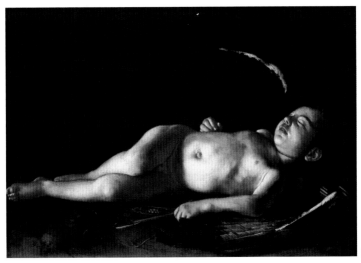

III-10

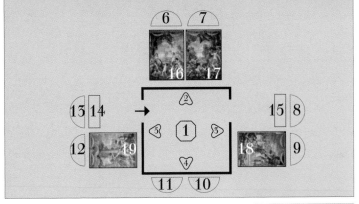

Stove Room (Sala della Stufa)

The ceiling of this room, originally an open loggia, was decorated between 1625 and 1627 by Michelangelo Cinganelli, Matteo Rosselli and Ottavio Vannini with allegories of the great monarchies of antiquity. The stuccoes are by Antonio Novelli and Sebastiano Pettirossi. At the end of this first phase of decorative work the loggia was closed off in 1627 and converted into a "stove" room, or rather the Grand Duke's bathroom.

The majolica-tiled floor was laid in 1627 by craftsmen from Montelupo, based on designs by Giulio Parigi. It was redone at the beginning of the twentieth century by the Florentine Cantagalli manufactory, except for the middle part with the *Triumph of the Monarchy*. Other fragments of the original flooring have been recovered from storage and are on display in the Hall of the Del Moro Staircase nearby.

Pietro da Cortona was asked to decorate the walls in 1637 with *The Four Ages of Man*, a theme inspired by Ovid and proposed by Michelangelo Buonarroti the Younger. The *Golden Age* alludes to Grand Duke Ferdinando II 's happy reign and the union in marriage of the Medici and Della Rovere families. It was done at the same time as the *Silver Age* during the artist's first stay in Florence (1637), while the *Bronze Age* and the *Iron Age* were completed in 1641.

The four niches either side of the two windows hold marble female figures, Roman works of art from the Imperial era.

Ceiling decorations

1 - *Fame*
2 - *Fortitude*
3 - *Fortune*
4 - *Justice*
5 - *Prudence*
6 - *Monarchy of the Romans*
7 - *Monarchy of the Saracens*
8 - *Monarchy of the Turks*
9 - *Monarchy of Austria*
10 - *Monarchy of the Assyrians*
11 - *Monarchy of the Medes*
12 - *Monarchy of the Persians*
13 - *Monarchy of the Macedonians*

Above the entrance way

14 - *Allegory of Trade*

Above the exit way

15 - *Allegory of Justice*

**Frescos
on the walls
from the left as you enter
(clockwise)**

Pietro da Cortona
16 - *Golden Age*
17 - *Silver Age*
18 - *Bronze Age*
19 - *Iron Age*

Hall of the Del Moro Staircase
(Atrio dello Scalone Del Moro)

The entrance to the new Palatine Gallery had been planned by the Hapsburg Lorraines with the project entrusted to Pasquale Poccianti in 1831, although by 1835 it had only been partially completed. It was not until the Savoys came to power that the architect Luigi del Moro, in 1892, designed the current monumental staircase in a neo-Renaissance style. It was completed five years later.

Antonio Rossellino and Benedetto da Maiano
Fountain with Medici coats of arms and devices

Artist from Tribolo's circle
Putto with Upper Bowl
Formerly in the Medici Villa of Castello, this work was placed here in 1889

Montelupo manufactory from a design by Giulio Parigi (1627)
Fragments of the original tiled floor of the Stove Room
glazed terracotta

Florentine manufactory, 17th century
Cabinet in the form of Palazzo Pitti
unpainted walnut wood

Florentine manufactory, 18th–19th century
Model of Palazzo Pitti
painted cypress wood

97

Iliad Room (Sala dell'Iliade)

In 1815 Ferdinand II of Hapsburg Lorraine incorporated this room into the Gallery's "Rooms of the Planets". It was divided into several areas, one of which was set aside by Cosimo III de' Medici in 1689 as a room for the 'gioco del trucco' (a game similar to billiards played at the time), and another as a private chapel. The ceiling, painted by Luigi Sabatelli, portrays episodes from the 15th book of the *Iliad* by Homer about the Trojan War, with Jupiter in the centre surrounded by the gods of Olympus.

In the centre of the room

Lorenzo Bartolini
Charity
marble, inv. OdA 1911
no. 1538
c. 1835
doc. at Palazzo Pitti in 1836
L II. AL

Wall I

I-1
Jacopo Bassano's
studio, 16th century
Parable of the Sower
canvas, inv. 1912 no. 177
GPF. M (1698)

I-2
Battista Franco (known as Il Semolei)
Battle of Montemurlo
wood panel, inv. 1912
no. 144
c. 1537
doc. at Palazzo Pitti in 1561
C I. M (1557)

I-3
Frans Francken II
Ascent to Calvary
wood panel, inv. 1912
no. 445
doc. at Palazzo Pitti in 1834

I-4
Annibale Carracci
Christ in Glory with Saints
canvas, inv. 1912 no. 220
c. 1597–1598
GPF. M
This painting was commissioned in 1597–1598 by Cardinal Odoardo Farnese (1573–1626) when the artist was in Rome. The Cardinal is in the composition on the bottom right in a praying position as he is presented to Christ by St. Edward of England. Although the painting may originally have been intended for the Villa di Caprarola, it was sent by the prelate to his cell dedicated to St. Mary Magdalene in the monastery of Camaldoli. At

the end of the seventeenth century Grand Prince Ferdinando obtained it for his own collection and from that moment onwards its home has been Palazzo Pitti.

I-5
Frans Pourbus the Younger
Portrait of Henrietta Maria of France
canvas, inv. 1890 no. 2401
c. 1612
doc. at Palazzo Pitti in 1687 (?)

I-4

I-6
Frans Pourbus the
Younger
*Portrait of
Eleonora Gonzaga*
canvas, inv. 1912 no. 391
c. 1603

I-7
Jan Cornelisz
Vermeyen
Portrait of a Man
wood panel, inv. 1912 no. 223
c. 1530
doc. from 1793; doc. at
Palazzo Pitti in 1833

I-8
Raphael
*Portrait of a Woman
(The Pregnant Woman)*
wood panel, inv. 1912 no. 229
C. M (1666)
This portrait depicts a
wealthy woman with her
left hand resting on her
pregnant belly. It is sty-
listically and typologically
close to the *Portraits of
Agnolo and Maddalena
Doni*, both works dating to
1506–1507 during the latter
part of Raphael's Floren-
tine period. Its admission
into the Medici collections
dates back to 1666, when
it was documented as be-
ing among Cardinal Carlo
de' Medici's works of art.

I-9
Andrea del Sarto
*Assumption of the Virgin
(Assunta Passerini)*
wood panel, inv. 1912 no. 225
FII. M (1639)
This altarpiece was com-
missioned in 1526 from
Andrea del Sarto by Margherita Passerini, the mother
of Cardinal Silvio, Bishop
of Cortona and Governor
of Florence. It was paired
with a magnificent vest-
ment based on a drawing
by Raffaellino del Garbo

I-8

I-9

99

and Andrea del Sarto, now on display in the Museum of Cortona. This painting on wood, placed in the church of Santa Maria dei Servi in Cortona in 1528, replicates the composition of the *Assunta Panciatichi*, which was done slightly earlier. St. Nicholas and St. Margaret (Margherita) are in the foreground, the latter evoking the buyer of the work. In 1639 it is said to have arrived in Grand Duke Ferdinando II 's collection as a gift from one of the heirs.

I-10
Frans Pourbus the Younger
Portrait of Christine of France
canvas, inv. 1890 no. 2407
c. 1612

I-11
Northern Italian school of the 16th century
Portrait of a Man as a Warrior Saint
wood panel, inv. 1912 no. 194
doc. from 1769; doc. at Palazzo Pitti in 1781

I-12
Justus Suttermans
Portrait of Domenico Cresti (il Passignano)
canvas, inv. 1890 no. 565
c. 1635
L. M. (1675)

I-13
Ridolfo del Ghirlandaio (?)
Portrait of a Woman
wood panel, inv. 1912 no. 224
dated 1509
V. DR (1631)
doc. at Palazzo Pitti in 1839

I-14
Niccolò Soggi
Madonna and Child enthroned, St. John the Baptist and St. Eustace (?)
wood panel, inv. 1912 no. 77
c. 1510
doc. from 1786; doc. at Palazzo Pitti in 1806

I-15
Carlo Dolci
St. John the Evangelist
canvas, inv. 1912 no. 217
signed and dated 1671
doc. from 1704
C III. M (1687)

I-16
Girolamo da Carpi
Portrait of Bishop Onofrio Bartolini Salimbeni
wood panel, inv. 1912 no. 36
c. 1524
doc. from 1704; doc. at Palazzo Pitti from 1819

I-17
Justus Suttermans
Portrait of Mattias de' Medici
canvas, inv. 1912 no. 265
c. 1660

II-1
after Titian
copy of the *Portrait of Paul III*
wood panel, inv. 1912 no. 326
16th century
V. DR (1631)
doc. at Palazzo Pitti in 1761

II-2
Titian
Portrait of a Man
canvas, inv. 1912 no. 215
c. 1540–1550
doc. from 1621; doc. at Palazzo Pitti in 1678

II-3
Federico Barocci (?)
copy of the *Madonna of St. James* by Correggio
canvas, inv. 1912 no. 214
GPF. M (1699)

II-4
Scipione Pulzone
Portrait of a Woman
wood panel, inv. 1912 no. 205
signed and dated 1595 (?)

II-5
Scipione Pulzone
Portrait of a Woman
wood panel, inv. 1912
no. 210
c. 1570
doc. at Palazzo Pitti in
1819

II-6
Justus Suttermans
*Portrait of Emperor
Ferdinand II of Austria*
canvas, inv. 1912 no. 209
1623
L. M (1675)

II-7
Carlo Dolci
Moses
canvas, inv. 1912 no. 213
c. 1645
doc. from 1691
V. DR (1695)

II-8

II-8
Fra' Bartolomeo
*Madonna and Child
enthroned with Saints
(Pitti Altarpiece)*
wood panel, inv. 1912
no. 208
signed and dated 1512
GPF. M (1690)

This large altarpiece,
signed and dated 'ORATE
PRO PICTORE 1512', was
done for the altar of Saint
Catherine in the Church
of San Marco in Florence.
It was a substitute for the
one done the previous year
for the same altar, given by
the Signoria to the French
ambassador (now in the
Louvre). In 1690 Grand
Prince Ferdinando de'
Medici persuaded the
Pope to intervene and suc-
ceeded in having the work
awarded to him. He had
it transferred to his own
apartments in Palazzo Pitti,
widening it and providing
it with its current frame for
display purposes.

II-9
Cristofano
dell'Altissimo
*Portrait of Francesco I
de' Medici*
wood panel, inv. 1912 no. 206
c. 1562
F I. M (before 1609)

II-10
Scipione Pulzone
Portrait of a Woman
wood panel, inv. 1912 no. 211
c. 1595

II-11
Justus Suttermans
*Portrait of Eleonora
Gonzaga*
canvas, inv. 1912 no. 203
1623
L. M (1675)

II-12
Ridolfo del Ghirlandaio
*Portrait of a Man
(The Goldsmith)*
wood panel, inv. 1912 no. 207
c. 1515–1517
L. M (1668)

II-13
Giovanni Bilivert
*Archangel Raphael
refusing Tobias' gifts*
canvas, inv. 1912 no. 202
dated 1612, initialled: GB
L II. AL (1832)

II-14
Artemisia Gentileschi
St. Mary Magdalene
canvas, inv. 1912 no. 142
c. 1620
signed

II-15
Titian and studio
*Portrait of Philip II
of Spain*
canvas, inv. 1912 no. 200
c. 1550
doc. from 1560; doc. at
Palazzo Pitti in 1687
C I. M

Wall III

III-1

Jacopo and Francesco Bassano's studio, 16th century
Christ in the house of Martha and Mary
canvas, inv. 1912 no. 236
doc. from 1723

III-2

Justus Suttermans
Portrait of Leopoldo de' Medici
canvas, inv. 1890 no. 4345
c. 1660

III-3

Artemisia Gentileschi
Judith with the head of Holofernes
canvas, inv. 1912 no. 398
doc. at Palazzo Pitti in 1637
CII. M ?

This painting is one of the most renowned works done by the daughter of the artist Orazio Gentileschi. Artemisia Gentileschi was already in Florence in September 1613 in the service of the Grand Duke Cosimo II. She is thought to have painted this composition between 1613 and 1618 for the Grand Duke, recapturing the elegant and bright Caravaggism of her father in the biblical heroine and the maidservant with Holofernes' head in the basket. The work is documented as being at Palazzo Pitti from 1637 onwards.

III-4

Paolo Veronese and studio
St. Benedict and Saints
canvas, inv. 1912 no. 196
dated 1572
doc. from 1648; doc. at Palazzo Pitti in 1699
GPF. M (1699)

III-5

Venetian school (?), 16th century
Portrait of a Man
canvas, inv. 1912 no. 193
doc. at Palazzo Pitti in 1828

III-6

Frans Pourbus the Younger (?)
Portrait of Maria de' Medici

III-3

III

canvas, inv. 1912 no. 192
c. 1610
doc. from 1810

III-7
Andrea del Sarto
Madonna and Child
wood panel, inv. 1912
no. 476
1528–1530
F I. M (1579)

III-8
Andrea del Sarto
*Assumption of the
Virgin (Assunta
Panciatichi)*
wood panel, inv. 1912 no. 191
MM. A (1602); GPF. M
(1687)
This altarpiece was originally intended for the altar
of the Panciatichi chapel
in the Church of Notre-
Dame de Confort in Ly-
ons. It was commissioned
in 1522 by the Florentine
merchant Bartolomeo the
Elder but it never reached
its destination because of
defects in the wood panel
prepared by the renowned
carpenter and architect
Baccio d'Agnolo. After
various changes in own-
ership it was bought in
1602 by Grand Duchess
Maria Magdalena of Aus-
tria, consort of Cosimo II,
and joined Grand Prince
Ferdinando de' Medici's
collection in 1687.

III-9
Emilian school,
17th century
*Portrait of Scipione
Nerchi Mutolo*
canvas, inv. 1912 no. 189
doc. at Palazzo Pitti in 1828

III-10
Frans Pourbus the
Younger
*Portrait of Eleonora
de' Medici*
canvas, inv. 1912 no. 187

III-8

c. 1600–1609
doc. 1645
L. M (1675)

III-11
Justus Suttermans
*Portrait of Valdemar
Christian of Denmark*
canvas, inv. 1912 no. 190
1638–1639
F II. M

III-12
Paolo Veronese
Baptism of Christ
canvas, inv. 1912 no. 186
F I. M (1668); GPF. M
This painting came to Pal-
azzo Pitti from Ancona in
1668 when it was bought by
Grand Duke Ferdinando II
de' Medici. It then passed

into the collection of Grand
Prince Ferdinando, who
had it widened to match
the dimensions of the *St.
Benedict and Saints*, a work
by the same artist with the
help of his studio, which
was bought by the Grand
Prince in 1699 and put
on display in this room. It
is believed to be the late
work of Veronese due to
its stylistic similarity to
the *Magdalene* in the Prado
Museum dated 1583.

III-13
Francesco Bassano
Oration in the Garden
canvas, inv. 1912 no. 443
c. 1580–1590
doc. 1660
V. DR (1691)

103

III-14
Justus Suttermans
Portrait of Ferdinando II de' Medici
canvas, inv. 1912 no. 415
c. 1635
L. M (1675)

III-15
Diego Velázquez (?)
Portrait of Philip IV of Spain on horseback
canvas, inv. 1912 no. 243
c. 1635–1637
doc. at Palazzo Pitti in 1828

Wall IV

IV-1
Rosso Fiorentino
Madonna and Child with Saints (Dei Altarpiece)
wood panel, inv. 1912, no. 237
GPF. M (1691)

This altarpiece, signed and dated 1522, was done for the chapel of the Dei family in the Church of Santo Spirito after Raphael, in 1508, left the previous panel unfinished (better known as the *Madonna of the Baldachin* – now on display in the Saturn Room). This work, a masterpiece of early maturity, is remarkable for the crowd of saints around the Madonna and Child, conceived by the artist, and for its bright and vivid colours. The altarpiece was enlarged on all sides and painted in by Niccolò

Cassana for reasons of symmetry with the other monumental works in the collection of Grand Prince Ferdinando, who bought it in 1691.

IV-2
after Titian, 17th century
copy of the *Bacchus and Ariadne*
canvas, inv. 1912 no. 157
doc. from 1638
GPF. M (1697)

IV-3
Domenichino
St. Mary Magdalene
canvas, inv. 1912 no. 176
c. 1620–1630
F III. AL (1819)

IV-4
Paolo Veronese
Presentation of Jesus at the Temple
canvas, inv, 1912 no. 269
F II - F III AL (1793)

IV-

Saturn Room (Sala di Saturno)

This room takes its name from the god Saturn who is depicted on the ceiling welcoming the now elderly Medici Prince; the ceiling was painted by Ciro Ferri between 1663 and 1665 from drawings by Pietro da Cortona. This room brings to an end the sequence of rooms of the five planets frescoed by Pietro da Cortona and was formerly intended for the private audiences of Grand Duke Ferdinando II, who commissioned the work.

Wall I

I-1
Justus Suttermans
Portrait of Anna de' Medici
canvas, inv. 1912 no. 323
c. 1635

I-2
Florentine school (?), 17th century
Portrait of an Artist
canvas, inv. 1912 no. 447
doc. in 1704; doc. at Palazzo Pitti in 1828

I-3
Carlo Dolci
Portrait of Vittoria della Rovere
canvas, inv. 1912 no. 404
c. 1680
doc. at Palazzo Pitti in 1702–1710
C III. M

I-4
Sebastiano del Piombo
Martyrdom of St. Agatha
wood panel, inv. 1912 no. 179
signed and dated 1520
doc. in 1624
V. DR (1631)

I-5
Justus Suttermans
Portrait of Canon Pandolfo Ricasoli
canvas, inv. 1912 no. 401
c. 1630
F II. M

I-6
Jacopo Bassano
Adam and Eve
canvas, inv. 1912 no. 170
c. 1560
L. M (1654)

I-7
Raphael
Madonna and Child (Madonna of the Grand Duke)
wood panel, inv. 1912 no. 178
F III. AL (1799)
This painting was done between 1506 and 1508, and was originally intended for the private devotion of a Florentine family. It was bought in Florence in 1799 and sent to Grand Duke Ferdinand II of Hapsburg Lorraine, then in exile, who kept it with him at all times among his most precious things (hence the name of the *Madonna of the Grand Duke*). The dark background does not seem to belong to the original and could be the result of tampering in the seventeenth century due to changing tastes and commercial considerations.

I-7

105

I-8
Andrea del Sarto
Disputation on the Trinity
wood panel, inv. 1912 no. 172
c. 1517
C. L

This signed altarpiece was done around 1517 for the Peri altar in the Augustinian Church of San Gallo, and shows St. Augustine speaking to St. Lawrence, St. Peter Martyr, St. Francis, St. Mary Magdalene and St. Sebastian about the mystery of the Trinity, depicted on a smaller scale with God the Father and Christ in a cloud which alludes to the Holy Spirit. After being transferred in 1529 to the Church of San Jacopo tra' Fossi, it was brought to Palazzo Pitti in 1626 by Grand Duchess Christine of Lorraine, widow of Grand Duke Ferdinando I.

I-8

I-9
Guercino's studio
Saint Peter in Tears
wood panel, inv. 1912 no. 168
mid-17th century
doc. in 1706
GPF. M (1713)

I-10
Sodoma's studio
Ecce Homo
wood panel, inv. 1912 no. 374
mid-16th century

I-11
Annibale Carracci
Head of a Man
canvas, inv. 1912 no. 166
c. 1590–1592

I-12
Domenico Puligo
Holy Family with the Young St. John
wood panel, inv. 1912 no. 169
c. 1525
doc. in 1589; doc. at Palazzo Pitti in 1791

I-1

I-13
Jacopo Bassano's
studio
Parable of the Sower
canvas, inv. 1912 no. 177
second half of the
16th century
doc. at Palazzo Pitti in 1829

I-14
Raphael
*Portrait of Tommaso
'Fedra' Inghirami*
wood panel, inv. 1912 no. 171
L. M

The man in this portrait
was a poet and a cultured
friend of Leo X Medici. He
was known as Fedra (Phae-
dra) because he acted the
part to great acclaim in a
production of *Hippolytus*
by Senaca. In 1510 he was
nominated Prefect of the
Vatican Library, and probably wanted to celebrate the
event by having his portrait
done by Raphael. The por-
trait was bought by Cardinal
Leopoldo de' Medici during
the seventeenth century and
is now recognised as the
original version as opposed
to the other version in the
Isabella Stewart Gardner
Museum in Boston.

Wall II

II-1
Raphael
*Madonna and Child
Enthroned with Saints*

*(Madonna of the
Baldachin)*
wood panel, inv. 1912
no. 165
1507–1508
GPF. M (1697)

Commissioned by the Dei
family for its altar in the
Church of Santo Spirito
around 1507, this altarpiece
was left unfinished by Raphael when he left for Rome
the following year. The task
is then thought to have

passed to Rosso Fiorenti-
no, the creator of the final
altarpiece which is signed
and dated 1522 and is also
on display here in the Gallery in the Iliad Room. It
was placed in Pescia Cathedral and is thought to have
remained there until 1697
when Grand Prince Fer-
dinando de' Medici had it
transferred to Palazzo Pitti,
enlarging it on all sides for
reasons of symmetry.

II-1

II-2
Raphael
Portrait of Agnolo Doni
wood panel, inv. 1912
no. 61
LII. AL

This portrait of Agnolo, with that of his consort Maddalena Strozzi, was commissioned from Raphael around 1505. It contains an omen of fertility for the married couple in the *Universal Flood* and the *Rebirth of Mankind after the Flood* painted in chiaroscuro on the reverse by the so-called Maestro di Serumido. These portraits were probably positioned in the couple's wedding chamber in the same place as the *Doni Tondo* by Michelangelo in the Uffizi. They were sold in 1826 by the heirs of Grand Duke Leopold II of Hapsburg Lorraine.

II-3
Raphael
Vision of Ezekiel
wood panel, inv. 1912
no. 174
Fr I. M

The iconography of this little painting is disputed. It is traditionally identified with the apparition of the Eternal Father in glory, with the symbols of the four evangelists, to the prophet Ezekiel. The small figure on the lower left side could, however, be Saint John the Evangelist, who had an identical vision on the island of Patmos described in the Book of Revelation. The painting was done between 1516 and 1518 for Vincenzo Ercolani, a man from Bologna, and given in the 1570s by his brother, an ambassador to Florence, to Grand Duke Francesco I de' Medici.

II-4
Raphael
Portrait of Maddalena Doni
wood panel, inv. 1912
no. 59
LII. AL
See painting at no. II-2.

II-5
Perugino
Lamentation over the Dead Christ
wood panel, inv. 1912
no. 164
signed and dated 1495

This large painting on wood, signed and dated 1495, is one of Perugino's most famous works. It was painted for the Church of Santa Chiara, a centre of Savonarolian devotion and piety where the *Adoration of the Shepherds* by Lorenzo di Credi in the Uffizi could also be found. It was bought in 1808 after the dissolution of the Church and the Monastery, and came to the Accademia Gallery, thence to Palazzo Pitti where it appears in records in 1819.

II-6
Fra' Bartolomeo
Resurrected Christ with the Four Evangelists (Salvator mundi)
wood panel transferred to canvas, inv. 1912 no. 159
signed and dated 1516
C. M (*c.* 1631)

II-5

II-7
Justus Suttermans
Virgin Mary
canvas, inv. 1912 no. 160
L. M (1675)

II-8
Bonifacio Veronese
*Moses Saved from the
Water*
wood panel, inv. 1912 no. 161
c. 1540
L. M (1675)

II-9
Federico Barocci's
studio
Portrait of a Man
canvas, inv. 1912 no. 162
V. DR (1631)

On the console table

Valsoldo (?)
Portrait of Pope Leo XI
marble, inv. Sculture no. 175
c. 1605
doc. at Palazzo Pitti in 1793

Wall III

III-1
Florentine school,
16th century
Portrait of a Woman
wood panel, inv. 1912 no. 439
c. 1580–1590

III-2
Pier Francesco Mola (?)
A Poet Laureate
canvas, inv. 1912 no. 181
doc. at Palazzo Pitti in
1828

III-3
Raphael (?)
*Portrait of Cardinal
Bernardo Dovizi of
Bibbiena*
canvas, inv. 1912 no. 158
GC. M (1637)

II-3

II-5

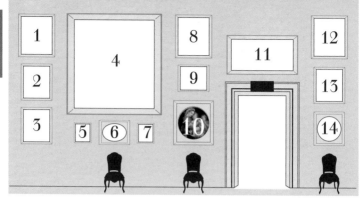

III-4
Andrea Schiavone
Cain and Abel
canvas, inv. 1912 no. 152
c. 1542
L. M (1664)

III-5
Carlo Dolci
St. Rose of Lima
canvas, inv. 1912 no. 155
1668

III-6
Carlo Dolci
The Sleep of St. John
canvas, inv. 1912 no. 154
c. 1670–1674
V. DR

III-1

III-7
after Correggio
Putto
wood panel, inv. 1912
no. 153
doc. at Palazzo Pitti in
1715–1723
C III. M

III-8
Empoli
Portrait of Giovan
Battista Gambetti
wood panel, inv. 1890
no. 2124
signed and dated 1594
doc. in 1814; doc. at Palazzo Pitti in 1828

III-9
Giovanni da San
Giovanni's circle
Madonna and Child
canvas, inv. 1912 no. 396
first half of the
17th century
L. M (1675)

III-10
Raphael
Madonna and Child
with the Young St. John
(Madonna of the
Chair)
wood panel, inv. 1912 no. 151
c. 1513–1514
FI. M (1589)

This highly renowned mas-
terpiece, a tondo, painted
in 1513–1514, shows the
Virgin Mary dressed in the
brightly coloured clothes

of a country woman, but
seated on a "chamber"
chair normally reserved
for members of the Papal
court (hence the name of
the work). A plump Baby
Jesus sits in her lap and
the Young St. John watches
them as he prays in a composition of full of loving in-
timacy. In all likelihood this
work was commissioned by
Pope Leo X Medici and it
is documented as being in
the Medicean collections
from 1589 onwards during
the reign of Grand Duke
Ferdinando I de' Medici.

III-11
Andrea del Sarto
Annunciation
wood panel, inv. 1912 no. 163
1528
doc. in 1534
F I. M. (1584)

III-12
Orlando Flacco
Portrait of a Woman
canvas, inv. 1912 no. 414
doc. at Palazzo Pitti in
1744
GC. M

III-13
Perugino's studio
Madonna and Child
with two Saints
wood panel, inv. 1912
no. 540
c. 1490–1500
doc. at Palazzo Pitti in 1806

III-14
Francesco
Montemezzano
Portrait of a Woman
canvas, inv. 1912 no. 37
L. M (1675)

Wall IV

IV-1
Guercino
St. Sebastian
canvas, inv. 1912 no. 490
1652
GC. M (1653)

IV-2
Alessandro Tiarini
Adam and Eve
Mourning Abel
canvas, inv. 1912 no. 488
c. 1630–1640
doc. at Palazzo Pitti in
1698

On the console tables

Ottaviano Giovannozzi
Bust of Leopold II of
Lorraine
marble, inv. 1912 no. 885
signed and dated 1823

Ottaviano Giovannozzi
Bust of Ferdinand II of
Lorraine
marble, inv. 1912 no. 886
signed and dated 1822

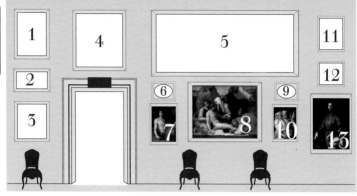

Jupiter Room (Sala di Giove)

This room and the Saturn Room were originally intended by Ferdinando II de' Medici to be his public and private audience rooms. Upon the Grand Duke's request, Pietro da Cortona frescoed the ceiling between 1642 and 1644 with the coronation of the young Prince by Jupiter, father of the gods, thus emphasising the regal function of the room.

In the centre of the room

Vincenzo Consani
Victory
marble, inv. OdA 1911
no. 1540
1867

Wall I

I-1
Guercino and studio
Madonna and Child with an Angel (Madonna of the Swallow)
canvas, inv. 1912 no. 156
L. M (1675)
doc. at Palazzo Pitti in 1687

I-2
Guercino
Holy Family
canvas, inv. 1912 no. 132
c. 1615–1616
doc. at Palazzo Pitti in 1819

I-3
Perugino
Adoration of the Child (Madonna of the Sack)
wood panel, inv. 1912 no. 219
c. 1500

I-7

doc. in 1635; doc. at Palazzo Pitti in 1819

I-4
Carlo Dolci
St. Peter in Tears
canvas, inv. 1912 no. 91
dated on reverse 1654
V. DR (1691)

I-5
Peter Paul
Rubens' studio
Nymphs and Satyrs
canvas, inv. 1912 no. 141
GPF. M (1698)

I-6
Francesco Albani
Holy Family with two Angels
copper, inv. 1912 no. 175
V. DR (1691)

I-7
Andrea del Sarto
St. John the Baptist
wood panel, inv. 1912 no. 272
C I. M (1553)

This panel constituted the middle part of a backboard above a chest made by Baccio d'Agnolo in the antechamber of Giovan Maria Benintendi's house. It was surrounded by the *Adoration of the Magi* by Pontormo (on display in the Prometheus Room, I-5), the *Baptism of Christ* by Bacchiacca in Berlin, the *Legend of the Dead King* by Bacchiacca in Dresden and the *Bathsheba* by Franciabigio. The *Bathsheba* is the only work to bear a date, 1523, which can almost certainly be used as a reference for all the paintings.

I-8
Fra' Bartolomeo
Lamentation over the Dead Christ
wood panel, inv. 1912 no. 64
1511
C. M (1619)

I-8

This painting on wood was done around 1511 for the main altar of the Church of San Gallo. It was transferred in 1529, following the destruction of the Church during the siege of Florence, to the Church of San Jacopo tra' Fossi before being bought in 1619 by Cardinal Carlo de' Medici. It was shortened by about a third of its height, taking away the heads of St. Peter and St. Paul and the background; it was painted over in black with only the figures in the foreground spared. Following its recent restoration, during which this overpainting was removed, the original, highly devout composition was recovered, though reduced to a fragment.

I-9
Francesco Albani
Resurrected Christ appears to the Virgin
copper, inv. 1912 no. 173
c. 1650–1660
doc. at Palazzo Pitti in 1799
GPF. M

I-10
Francesco Salviati
The Three Fates
wood panel, inv. 1912 no. 113
This painting, with its rare iconography, depicts the three Parcae or Fates, mythological figures who were believed have the

I-10

power of deciding how long every mortal would live. Clotho is depicted with the distaff, Lachesis is holding the thread and Atropos is cutting it. The work belonged to the collection of Grand Prince Ferdinando de' Medici where it was attributed to Michelangelo, though it is now commonly believed to be a work of Salviati's full maturity and can be dated to around 1550.

I-11
Cigoli
Portrait of a Man
canvas, inv. 1912 no. 226
signed and dated 1594
L. M (1675)

I-12
Cesare Gennari
Holy Family
canvas, inv. 1912 no. 332
signed and dated 1674
L. M (1674)

113

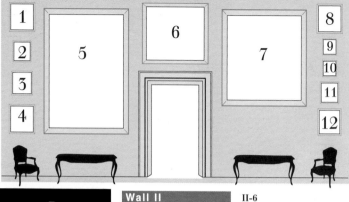

I-13

I-13
Bronzino
*Portrait of
Guidobaldo II della
Rovere*
wood panel, inv. 1912
no. 149
V. DR (1631)
This portrait of the heir to
the throne of Urbino was
done in Pesaro by Bronzino
before 1552 when the sub-
ject was 18 years old (as
stated by the accompa-
nying Latin inscription).
In addition, the motto in
Greek 'it will be as I wish'
is intended as a good omen
for the young man's des-
tiny. Guidobaldo asked the
painter to await the ar-
rival of a magnificent suit
of armour which had been
sent for from Lombardy as
a birthday gift, thought by
some to be one of a similar
description in the Musée de
l'Armée in Paris.

Wall II

II-1
Justus Suttermans
*Portrait of the Steward
Leonido*
canvas, inv. 1912 no. 419
c. 1620–1630
doc. at Palazzo Pitti in
1687

II-2
Carlo Dolci
Portrait of a Man
canvas, inv. 1912 no. 316
doc. in 1649

II-3
Justus Suttermans'
studio
*Portrait of Galileo
Galilei*
canvas, inv. 1912 no. 106
c. 1640
F II. M

II-4
Justus Suttermans
*Portrait of Captain Elia
da Zia*
canvas, inv. 1912 no. 119
c. 1630–1637
doc. at Palazzo Pitti in 1637

II-5
Fra' Bartolomeo
St. Mark
wood panel transferred to
canvas, inv. 1912 no. 125
1515
doc. in 1515
GPF. M (1690)

II-6
Andrea del Sarto
Annunciation
wood panel, inv. 1912 no. 124
signed
c. 1513–1514
MM. A (1627)

II-7
Andrea del Sarto
*Assumption of
the Virgin (Poppi
Altarpiece)*
wood panel, inv. 1912 no. 123
c. 1530
F III. AL (1818)

II-8
Justus Suttermans
*Portrait of
Ferdinando II de' Medici
dressed as a Turk*
canvas, inv. 1890 no. 2354
c. 1640–1642

II-9
after Annibale Carracci
copy of the *Madonna
and Child with the
Young St. John*
canvas, inv. 1912 no. 425
L. M. (1675)
doc. at Palazzo Pitti in 1761

II-10
Jacopo Vignali
*St. Francis of Assisi in
Ecstasy*
copper, inv. 1912 no. 356
c. 1620
L. M. (1675)

II-11
Augsburg school,
16th century
*Portrait of Jakobina
Ungelter*
canvas, inv. 1912 no. 33
c. 1556
GG. M

II-12
Andrea del Verrocchio
St. Jerome
paper affixed to wood
panel, inv. 1912 no. 370
c. 1460–1470
doc. at Palazzo Pitti in 1675
GC. M (1646)

Wall III

III-1
Domenico and Valore
Casini (?)
*Portrait of Simone
Paganucci*
canvas, inv. 1912 no. 117
GPF. M (1713)

III-2
Guercino
Moses
canvas, inv. 1912 no. 103
c. 1620–1630
doc. 1796

III-3
Peter Paul Rubens
*Holy Family with
St. Elizabeth and the
Young St. John (The
Madonna of the Basket)*
wood panel, inv. 1912
no. 139
c. 1615
doc. 1652; doc. at Palazzo
Pitti in 1761
GPF. M (1697)

III-4
Ambrogio Borgognone
Battle
canvas, inv. 1912 no. 112
c. 1650
doc. at Palazzo Pitti in 1824

III-7

III-5
Orazio Gentileschi
St. Agnes
wood panel, inv. 1912
no. 420
F II. M (1633)

III-6
Florentine school,
16th century
Double Portrait
wood panel, inv. 1912
no. 118
doc. at Palazzo Pitti in
1782
A. M (1588–1621)

III-7
Raphael
*Portrait of a Woman
(The Woman with the
Veil)*
canvas, inv. 1912 no. 245
C II. M (1620)
This portrait – one of
Raphael's greatest mas-
terpieces – was painted
around 1515 on canvas
in the Venetian style, like
the portrait of *Baldassare*

Castiglione at the Louvre.
The young girl is thought,
without foundation, to be
Raphael's mistress, traditionally identified as the
'bakeress' ('Fornarina').
This association is at odds
with the elegance of the
woman's gown with the
large white and gold dam-
ask sleeve, the magnifi-
cence and type of her jewels and the veil arranged
on her head in the style of
a married woman. Previ-
ously in the Botti collection
in Florence, this work came
to Palazzo Pitti in 1620 by
the hand of Grand Duke
Cosimo II de' Medici.

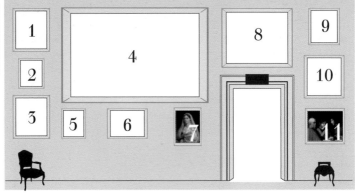

III-8
Niccolò Cassana
copy of the *Conspiracy of Catiline* by Salvator Rosa
canvas, inv. 1912 no. 111
GPF. M (1713)

III-9
Frans Pourbus the Younger
Portrait of a Man
canvas, inv. 1912 no. 244
c. 1600–1609
L. M (1675)

III-10
Paris Bordon
Portrait of a Woman
canvas, inv. 1912 no. 109
c. 1550–1555
L. M (1675)

III-11
Giorgione
The Three Ages of Man
wood panel, inv. 1912 no. 110
GPF. M (1698)
The figures in this composition allude to the three ages of Man and are gathered together around a sheet of music in the portrayal of a concert, a very popular subject in northern Italian painting. It was documented as being part of Grand Prince Ferdinando de' Medici's collection in 1698 and in spite of the damage caused by previous restorations, it maintains an atmosphere of mystery typical of the artist from Castelfranco Veneto. Giorgione absorbed this concept from Leonardo, who was in Venice in 1500.

III

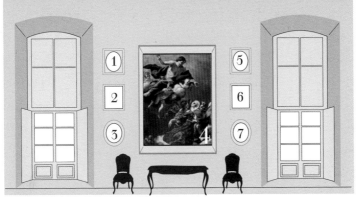

Wall IV

IV-1
after Guido Reni
St. Elizabeth
canvas, inv. 1912 no. 395
L. M (1675)

IV-2
after Federico Barocci
Christ Benedictory
canvas, inv. 1912 no. 101
V. DR (1631)

IV-3
Florentine school,
17th century
*St. Catherine of
Alexandria*
canvas, inv. 1890 no. 802
doc. at Palazzo Pitti in 1928

IV-4
Giovanni Lanfranco
*Ecstasy of St. Margaret
of Cortona*
canvas, inv. 1912 no. 318
GPF. M (1701-1702)
This work is signed and
dated 1622 and depicts the
Saint dressed in the clothing of the Franciscan terti-
ary, entranced by the vision
of Christ in glory among the
angels. On the lower left of
the painting a little dog is
holding the coat of arms of
the Venuti family, the buyers
of the work, which was intended for the family chapel
in the Church of Santa Maria
Nuova in Cortona. Between
1701 and 1702 it came into

the collection of Grand
Prince Ferdinando, who
had it replaced with a work
by Giuseppe Maria Crespi.

IV-5
Venetian school,
16th century
Portrait of a Man
canvas, inv. 1912 no. 390
L. M (1675)

IV-6
Bartolomeo Schedoni
Holy Family with the

Young St. John
wood panel, inv. 1912 no. 304
c. 1609
L. M (1675)

IV-7
Florentine school,
17th century
St. Agatha
canvas, inv. 1890 no. 803
doc. 1853; doc. at Palazzo
Pitti in 1928

IV-4

117

Mars Room (Sala di Marte)

This Room, formerly used as an antechamber to the Jupiter Room or Throne Room where the Grand Duke would give audience, was frescoed by Pietro da Cortona between 1643–1644 and 1647. The ceiling depicts a naval battle where a young prince defeats his enemies with the help of Mars. A large Medici coat of arms sits in the centre, held up by putti and adorned with the Grand-Ducal coronet.

Wall I

I-1
Cigoli
St. Mary Magdalene Penitent
canvas, inv. 1912 no. 98
c. 1600
doc. at Palazzo Pitti in 1663

I-2
Guercino's studio
St. Sebastian
canvas, inv. 1912 no. 99
1652
F III. AL

I-3
Andrea del Sarto
Annunciation with St. Michael Archangel and St. Gaudenzio
canvas, inv. 1912 no. 97
c. 1527–1528
CC. M (1627)

I-4
Pieter van Mol
St. Francis of Assisi in Ecstasy
canvas, inv. 1912 no. 93
initialled: P.V.MOL
GPF. M (1697)

I-

I-7

I-5
Bartolomé Esteban
Murillo
Madonna and Child
canvas, inv. 1912 no. 63
F III. AL (1822)

This world-famous paint-
ing, copied and reproduced
countless times, was the
first of two works to come
to the Palatine Gallery. It was
bought by the Grand Duke
of Tuscany Ferdinand II of
Hapsburg Lorraine and documented as already being
part of the collection in 1822.
It belongs to a group of Madonna and Child paintings
done by the Spanish artist
in his youth (1650–1655), including a work in the Prado
Museum; this painting is believed to be a later version.

I- 6
Ventura Salimbeni
*Holy Family with
St. Elizabeth and the
Young St. John*
canvas, inv. 1912 no. 45
signed and dated 1608
doc. in 1687

I-7
Peter Paul Rubens
*Self Portrait with the
Artist's Brother Philip,
Justus Lipsius and Jan
van den Wouvere (The
Four Philosophers)*
wood panel, inv. 1912
no. 85
doc. at Palazzo Pitti from
the end of the 17th century

This celebrated work is
documented as being in
the collections of Palazzo
Pitti at the end of the seventeenth century, although
its origin and buyer remain
unknown. The figures por-
trayed from left to right
include the artist and his
brother Philip (1574–1611),
who was a pupil of Justus
Lipsius (1547–1606), Lipsius

himself with the fur over-
coat, and lastly, Jan van den
Wouvere (1576–1635), also
a pupil of Lipsius. Given
that the two central figures
were already deceased
in 1611–1612, when this
work is believed to have
been painted, it takes on a
commemorative aspect for
an elite, intellectual group.
It may have been commis-
sioned from Rubens by Jan
van den Wouvere in memo-
ry of their deceased friends.

I-8
Jan van den Hoecke
copy of the *Madonna
and Child, St. Elizabeth
and the Young St. John*
by Rubens
canvas, inv. 1912 no. 235
GPF. M (1698)

I-9
Bartolomé Esteban
Murillo
*Madonna and Child
(Madonna of the
Rosary)*
canvas, inv. 1912 no. 56
c. 1648–1650
F III. AL (1822)

119

II-1
Fra' Bartolomeo
*Holy Family with
St. Elizabeth*
wood panel, inv. 1912 no. 256
c. 1516
doc. at Palazzo Pitti in 1663
GPF. M (1687)

II-2
Paolo Veronese
Portrait of a Man
canvas, inv. 1912 no. 216
L. M

This imposing portrait of a Venetian nobleman, once commonly believed to be Daniele Barbaro, was one of the most sought-after acquisitions of Prince Leopoldo de' Medici (later Cardinal) through his agent Paolo del Sera who, according to a letter addressed to Leopoldo, acquired the work in 1659. It is difficult to establish a date for this painting, varying as it does between 1550 and 1570. The work is notable for its fine chromatic range of greys and blacks which reveal influence from the portraiture of Titian and Tintoretto.

II-3
Peter Paul Rubens
The Consequences of War
canvas, inv. 1912 no. 86
1637
GPF. M (1691)

This is an allegorical portrayal of one of the most infamous horrors of the Thirty Years War. The painting was commissioned from Justus Suttermans in 1637 and shows Europe in black as she raises her eyes and arms to the heavens in front of the open-doored temple of Janus, while Venus endeavours to restrain Mars, armed and dragged by the Fury Alecto to battle. The painting was sent

to the buyer in 1638 before being obtained from the painter's heirs by Grand Prince Ferdinando for his own collection in 1691.

II-4, II-5
Andrea del Sarto
Stories from Joseph's Childhood

Joseph interprets the Pharaoh's Dream
wood panels, inv. 1912
nos. 88–87
Fr I. M (1584)

These two initialled and signed paintings on wood by Andrea Del Sarto, along with the two *Stories of Joseph* by Granacci at the Uffizi Gallery, are all that is left in Florence of the wooden furnishings made by Baccio d'Agnolo for the renowned bedchamber of Pierfrancesco Borgherini and Margherita Acciaiuoli, who married in 1515. The other paintings by Pontormo and Bachiacca are now divided between the National Gallery in London and the Borghese Gallery in Rome. In the first painting here in the Palatine Gallery, Joseph recounts his dreams to his father Jacob who, along with his wife Rachel, tells him to go to his brothers. His brothers are envious and throw him into a pit before selling him to the Ishmaelites and passing him off as dead. The second shows Joseph being led out of prison to explain the Pharaoh's dreams of the seven fat and lean cows and the seven full and withered ears of grain. The two paintings were bought in 1584 by Grand Duke Francesco I de' Medici.

II-4

II-5

II-7

II-6
Domenico Puligo
*Madonna and Child
with the Young St. John*
wood panel, inv. 1912
no. 242
c. 1512–1515
doc. in 1624; doc. at
Palazzo Pitti in 1798

II-7
Titian
*Portrait of Ippolito
de' Medici*
canvas, inv. 1912 no. 201
Cl. M (1553)

This portrait was docu-
mented for the first time
in 1553 in Duke Cosimo I
de' Medici's collection. It
was done in Venice in 1532
upon the return of the Cardinal, the natural son of
Giuliano, Duke of Nemours
(Florence 1511–Itri 1535),
from the victorious papal
expedition against the

Turks in Hungary. It was for
this reason that the Medici
Cardinal wished to have
himself painted dressed
in the Hungarian style
with his cuirass under his
clothing, a reinforced iron
mace in his right hand and
a curved sword in his left.
The clasp on Ippolito's hat
bears a pledge of his love
for Giulia Gonzaga.

On the table

Giovan Battista Foggini
Baptism of Christ
bronze, inv. Sculture
no. 1342
1723
AML. M

Wall III

III-1
Cigoli
Sacrifice of Issac
canvas, inv. 1912 no. 95
c. 1606–1607
doc. post 1616; doc. at Palazzo Pitti post 1798

III-2
Titian's studio
*Portrait of Andrea
Vesalio (?)*
canvas, inv. 1912 no. 80
c. 1545
doc. at Palazzo Pitti in
1702–1710
GPF. M

III-3
Adriaen van der Werff
*Portrait of John
Churchill Duke of
Marlborough*
canvas, inv. 1912 no. 76
signed and dated 1705
doc. in 1753

III-4
Anton van Dyck
*Portrait of Cardinal
Guido Bentivoglio*
canvas, inv. 1912 no. 82
F II. M (1653)

This painting was given in
1653 to Grand Duke Fer-
dinando II by Annibale
Bentivoglio, papal nuncio
to Florence from 1645 to
1652. It shows the Cardinal
(1577–1644) in the role of
protector of France at the
Holy See, a subject which
is referred to in the letter
on the table. Van Dyck
painted Bentivoglio with
great immediacy in 1622–
1623 shortly after he was
made Cardinal in 1621,
drawing on renowned
works by Titian, an artist
he greatly admired.

III-5
after Guido Reni
St. Peter in Tears
canvas, inv. 1912 no. 78
F III. AL (1818)

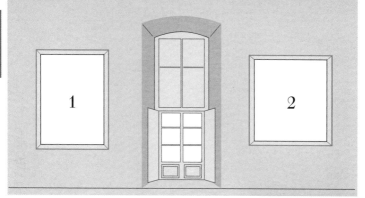

III-6
Tintoretto
Portrait of Alvise Cornaro
canvas, inv. 1912 no. 83
GPF. M (1698)

This portrait is now almost universally acknowledged to be Alvise Cornaro (Venice 1484–Padua 1566) an intellectual, collector and promoter of the figurative arts, known primarily for his *Treatise on the Sober Life* (Padua, 1558). Tintoretto must have painted him around 1565, as indicated by his advancing years, reaching one of the heights of his portraiture in terms of pictorial refinement and psychological insight. It is documented in 1698 as being in Grand Prince Ferdinando de' Medici's colletion.

III-7
Guido Cagnacci
St. Mary Magdalene taken up into the Sky by Angels
canvas, inv. 1912 no. 75
c. 1650–1658
GPF. M (1705)

III-8
Carlo Dolci
Portrait of a Woman as St. Margaret
canvas, inv. 1912 no. 227
inscribed: A salutis 1664...
principiavo...
doc. in 1695

III-9
Antiveduto Grammatica (?)
copy of *The Fortune Teller* by Simon Vouet
canvas, inv. 1912 no. 6
c. 1617
doc. at Palazzo Pitti in 1828
L.M (1675)

III-10
Bronzino
Portrait of Luca Martini
wood panel, inv. 1912 no. 434
c. 1554–1556
L.M (1675)

Wall IV

IV-1
Luca Giordano
Immaculate Madonna
canvas, inv. 1912 no. 104
1689
signed
doc. at Palazzo Pitti in 1798
C III. M (1687–1689)

IV-2
Giovanni Andrea Sirani
Rebecca at the Well
canvas, inv. 1912 no. 100
c. 1640
initialled: GR
doc. at Palazzo Pitti in 1761

III-4

III-6

Apollo Room (Sala di Apollo)

The decoration of the ceiling in this room, originally an antechamber for the "ordinary nobility", depicts a Medicean Prince guided by Fame in the presence of Apollo, who points out Hercules with the celestial sphere and the signs of the zodiac. The future sovereign thus had the weight of the responsibilities of government presaged to him along with the importance of being educated in the role by the Liberal Arts. The central fresco is surrounded by episodes of the myth of Apollo and the Muses and the great sovereigns of the past. Pietro da Cortona began the decorative work in 1647 and it was completed according to his designs by his pupil Ciro Ferri between 1659 and 1661.

Wall I

I-1
Justus Suttermans
Portrait of Francesco Maria de' Medici
canvas, inv. 1912 no. 344
c. 1663
doc. in 1663

I-2
after Andrea del Sarto
copy of the *Portrait of Baccio Bandinelli (?)*
canvas, inv. 1912 no. 66
doc. at Palazzo Pitti in 1797

I-3
Titian
St. Mary Magdalene
wood panel, inv. 1912 no. 67
signed
V. DR (1631)
This work, signed on the ointment jar, was painted around 1530 presumably for Francesco Maria della Rovere, Duke of Urbino and constituted the prototype

I-3

of a series of paintings in this style with devoutness masking sensual gratification. It came to Florence in 1631 with other paintings from the legacy of Grand Duchess Vittoria della Rovere, Ferdinando II's wife, now divided between the Palatine Gallery and the Uffizi Gallery.

I-4
Titian and studio
The Madonna of Mercy
canvas, inv. 1912 no. 484
c. 1573
V. DR (1631)

I-5
Andrea del Sarto
Holy Family with the Young St. John (Bracci Holy Family)
wood panel, inv. 1912 no. 62
c. 1523
doc. at Palazzo Pitti in 1761
F I. M (1579)

I-6
Titian
Portrait of a Man (The Englishman)
canvas, inv. 1912 no. 92
c. 1525
GPF. M (1698)

The identity of the blue-eyed young man in this portrait is unknown, though he is undoubtedly of noble origin as revealed by his clothing and gold necklace. Various names have been put forward but none have been substantiated. Painted around 1525, it remains one of Vecellio's masterpieces due to its naturalistic and immediate impact on the viewer and the aura of mystery encircling the subject, who stands out against the light background. The provenance of this work is unknown, though it is recorded as being part of Grand Prince Ferdinando's collection in 1698.

I-6

I-7
Andrea del Sarto
Lamentation over the Dead Christ (Pietà di Luco)
wood panel, inv. 1912 no. 58
PL. AL (1782)

This altarpiece was painted by Andrea del Sarto in 1523–1524 as a mark of gratitude for the hospitality he and his family received during the plague from the Camaldolite nuns of the Church of San Pietro di Luco in the Mugello region. Bought in 1782 by Grand Duke Peter Leopold of Lorraine, it is a masterpiece of the religious genre, with the crowds of saints around Christ's pale body revoked in the foreground by the Species on the paten and in the chalice.

I-7

I-8
Garofalo's studio
Augustus and the Sibyl
wood panel, inv. 1912
no. 122
post 1537
doc. at Palazzo Pitti in
1716–1723
L. M (1675)

I-9
Dosso Dossi
Nymph and Satyr
canvas, inv. 1912 no. 147
1508–1512
L. M (1675)

I-10
Ludovico Mazzolino
*Christ and the
Adulteress*
wood panel, inv. 1912
no. 129
c. 1526
L. M (1673); GPF. M
(1716–1723)

I-11
Caspar de Crayer
*Holy Family with the
Young St. John*
canvas, inv. 1890 no. 733
c. 1650
doc. in 1656; doc. at Palazzo Pitti in 1928

I-12
Tintoretto
*Portrait of Vincenzo
Zeno*
canvas, inv. 1912 no. 131
c. 1565

Wall II

II-1
Simone Cantarini
St. Andrew
canvas, inv. 1912 no. 48
c. 1640–1650
GPF. M (1699)

II-2
Dosso Dossi
St. John the Baptist
wood panel, inv. 1912
no. 380
doc. at Palazzo Pitti in
1855

II-8

126

II-3
Tiberio Titi
Portrait of Leopoldo de' Medici in his cradle
canvas, inv. 1912 no. 49
dated 1617
doc. 1640

II-4
Girolamo Denti (?)
Holy Family with St. Catherine of Alexandria and St. Mary Magdalene
canvas, inv. 1912 no. 52
c. 1550
GPF. M

II-5
Cigoli
Deposition from the Cross
wood panel, inv. 1912 no. 51
GPF. M (1690)
This magnificent altarpiece, with its elaborate composition and scenographic and dramatic quality, constitutes one of the heights of this master's ability and Florentine painting in the early seventeenth century. Painted for the Company of the Cross of Empoli over eight years between 1600 and 1608, this painting on wood attracted the attention of Grand Prince Ferdinando, who had it transferred to his own collection in Palazzo Pitti in 1690.

II-6
Guercino
St. Peter resuscitating Tabitha
canvas, inv. 1912 no. 50
c. 1618
GPF. M

II-7
Carlo Dolci
Diogenes
canvas, inv. 1912 no. 53
1640–1649
GPF. M. (1698)

II-8
Justus Suttermans
Portrait of Vittoria della Rovere as the Vestal Virgin Tuccia
canvas, inv. 1912 no. 116
c. 1640
doc. at Palazzo Pitti in 1688
L. M (1675)

II-9
Alessandro Vitali
Portrait of Federico Ubaldo della Rovere in his cradle
canvas, inv. 1912 no. 55
1605

Wall III

III-1
Niccolò Cassana
Portrait of an 'Alemannic soldier'
canvas, inv. 1912 no. 218
GPF. M (1691)

III-2
Andrea del Sarto
Madonna and Child, St. Elizabeth and the Young St. John (Medici Holy Family)
wood panel, inv. 1912 no. 81
1529
doc. at Palazzo Pitti in 1637
O. M (1550, 1568)

III-3
Cristofano Allori
The Hospitality of St. Julian
canvas, inv. 1912 no. 41
c. 1612–1618
F II. M (1658)

III-4
Giovanni Battista Langetti
Portrait of a Man (Sebastiano Mazzoni ?)
canvas, inv. 1912 no. 300
signed on reverse: Langetti
doc. at Palazzo Pitti in 1702–1710

III-5
Cristofano Allori
Portrait of a Man
canvas, inv. 1912 no. 72
c. 1600–1605
L. M (1675)

III-6
Peter Paul Rubens
Portrait of Kaspar Skoppe
canvas, inv. 1912 no. 198
c. 1606–1607

III-7
Guido Reni
Cleopatra
canvas, inv. 1912 no. 270
L. M (1640)

This sensual and dramatic subject with the suicide of the Queen of Egypt met with great success in the seventeenth century and the artist was asked to produce a great number of copies. This version, which belongs to the 'light' phase of his maturity, was painted between 1639 and 1640 on a commission from Marquis Ferdinando Cospi, a man from Bologna, who was acting on behalf of Cardinal Leopoldo de' Medici. The work is documented as being in the Cardinal's collection in 1640.

III-8
Jacopo Pistoia
Dinner at Emmaus
canvas, inv. 1912 no. 38
c. 1570–1572
initialled: JAP
doc. at Palazzo Pitti in 1663
C III. M (1716–1723)

III-9
Jacopo Ligozzi
Judith and Holofernes
canvas, inv. 1912 no. 444
signed and dated 1602
F I. M

III

III-10
Peter Paul Rubens
Portrait of Infanta Isabella Clara Eugenia
canvas, inv. 1890 no. 4263
c. 1625
V. DR (1654–1655)

III-11
Anton van Dyck's school
Portrait of Charles I and Henrietta Maria of England
canvas, inv. 1912 no. 150
doc. at Palazzo Pitti in 1687
C III. M ?

Wall IV

IV-1
Carlo Dolci
St. John the Evangelist
canvas, inv. 1912 no. 397
c. 1671
C III. M ?

IV-2
Cornelis de Vos
Portrait of a Woman
canvas, inv. 1912 no. 440
c. 1624

IV-3
after Sebastiano del Piombo
Ecce Homo
wood panel, inv. 1912 no. 322
C III. M (1685)

IV-4
Carlo Maratta
Vision of St. Philip Neri
canvas, inv. 1912 no. 71
GPF. M (1691)

This large painting was commissioned around 1670 by the Florentine senator Pietro Nerli for the altar of his own chapel in the Church of San Giovanni dei Fiorentini in Rome. The chapel was dedicated to St. Philip Neri, who is depicted as the Virgin Mary appears before him along

with her Son in glory, St. Mary Magdalene, St. Paul and St. Peter. It was given in 1691 by the son of the buyer, Peter, to Grand Prince Ferdinando de' Medici for his collection in Palazzo Pitti.

IV-5
Carlo Dolci
St. Casimir
canvas, inv. 1912 no. 392
1670–1671
doc. at Palazzo Pitti
in 1687
C III. M (1670)

IV-6
Jacob-Ferdinand Voet
Portrait of Olimpia Aldobrandini
canvas, inv. 1912 no. 34
c. 1665–1670

IV-7
Justus Suttermans
Portrait of Cavalier Brandolini
canvas, inv. 1912 no. 314
c. 1640–1650
doc. at Palazzo Pitti in
1702–1710

IV-4

129

Venus Room (Sala di Venere)

This room was used as an antechamber for the general public waiting to be received by Grand Duke Ferdinando II de' Medici and it is the first of five state apartments dedicated to the planets. The ceiling, decorated by Pietro da Cortona between 1641 and 1642, depicts a Prince being dragged from Venus' arms by Minerva to be given to Hercules, the titular numen of the Medici family. The lunettes hold paintings of virtues from antiquity and the medallions contain stucco figures of illustrious members of the Medici family.

In the centre of the room

Antonio Canova
Venus Italica
marble, inv. 1912 no. 878
This statue was initially commissioned from Canova as a copy of the *Medici Venus*, which was removed from the Tribune of the Uffizi Gallery and sent to France in 1802. It was sculpted between 1804 and 1811 as a free neoclassic interpretation of the Venus Pudica archetype (Modest Venus). In 1811 it was placed in the Tribune of the Uffizi Gallery and when the *Medici Venus* came back from Paris, it was moved to Palazzo Pitti to the Round Room of the Royal Apartments. Subsequently, after a period in the Flora Room, it was put on display in the centre of this room.

Wall I

I-1
Follower of Justus Suttermans (?)
Portrait of Giacinto Talducci
canvas, inv. 1890 no. 4271
C III. M

I-2
Emilian school,
16th century
Portrait of a Man
wood panel, inv. 1890 no. 3143
doc. in 1902; doc. at Palazzo Pitti in 1931

I-3
Pietro da Cortona
St. Martina refusing to worship Idols
canvas, inv. 1912 no. 21
C III. M (1674)

130

I-5

I-4
Justus Suttermans
*Portrait of Hunters
from the Medicean
Court*
canvas, inv. 1912 no. 137
c. 1637
doc. in 1637–1638
GC. M

I-5
Salvator Rosa
*Harbour with a
Lighthouse and Ships*
canvas, inv. 1912 no. 15
c. 1641
GC. M

This large painting was
conceived at the same
time as the *Seascape at
Sunset* (its counterpart or
pendant – see III-1), following the artist's stay at
Livorno in 1641 to draw the
ships moored there. The
Seascapes were commis-
sioned by Cardinal Giovan
Carlo de' Medici, and when
he died in 1663 they were
in his Hunting Lodge in
Via della Scala. The works
show the evident influence
of Lorrain's *Port with Medici Villa* at the Uffizi Gallery,
painted in 1637 for Cardinal
Carlo de' Medici.

I-6
Titian
*Portrait of a Woman
(La Bella Donna)*
canvas, inv. 1912 no. 18
VD. R (1631)
The identity of the young
women the artist depicted
here is unknown. Her

sumptuous clothes and
jewels have led to the idea
that she came from the
Della Rovere family or, at
any rate, that she was a
women of upper-class ori-
gin. This portrait was done
around 1536 for Frances-
co Maria I della Rovere,
Duke of Urbino. It came to

I-6

131

Florence in 1631 as part of the inheritance of Vittoria della Rovere, who married Grand Duke Ferdinando II de' Medici. The painting's recent restoration (2010) has unexpectedly brought to light the rich chromatic texture of the clothes and the clear, bright skin tones.

I-7
Bonifacio Veronese
Holy Conversation with Constantine, St. Helen and the Young St. John
wood panel, inv. 1912
no. 84
c. 1510
GPF. M (1713)

I-8
Titian
Portrait of Pietro Aretino
canvas, inv. 1912 no. 54
CI. M (1545)

This portrait was sent as a gift by Aretino himself to Cosimo I de' Medici in 1545; it had only just left the hands of his friend Titian, who had come to Rome in the service of Pope Paul III Farnese. The writer is depicted in his most

I-8

luxurious clothes and a big gold necklace, demonstrating his popularity with the sovereigns of Europe. Upon its arrival, however, the painting was not received with the appreciation expected and it was placed, in spite of Aretino's protestations, in inconsequential rooms within the Medicean household.

II-

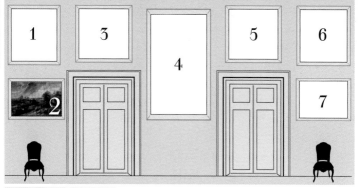

II-1
Matteo Rosselli
David's Triumph
canvas, inv. 1912 no. 13
c. 1620
doc. in 1620
C. M (1666)

II-2
Peter Paul Rubens
*Peasants returning
from the Fields*
wood panel, inv. 1912 no. 14
1635
FS. AL (1737)
Although both of a similar
size and although both belonged to Cardinal Richel-
ieu's collection, this painting and the *Ulysses on the
Island of the Phaeacians* (see
II-7) cannot be considered
as *pendants*, partly because
they can be dated to 1635
and 1627 respectively. The
two works both belonged
to the estate of the court of
Lunéville and came to Florence in 1737 on the order of
Francis Stephan of Lorraine,
who had just become Grand
Duke of Tuscany.

II-3
Rutilio Manetti
*Ruggiero at Alcina's
Court*
canvas, inv. 1912 no. 12
1624
signed
C. M (1622–1623)

II-4
Francesco Bassano
*Martyrdom of
St. Catherine of
Alexandria*
canvas, inv. 1912 no. 11
c. 1590
GPF. M (1698)

II-5
Giovanni Bilivert (?)
Apollo and Marcia
canvas, inv. 1912 no. 22

II-6
Guercino
Apollo and Marcia
canvas, inv. 1912 no. 8
c. 1618
doc. in 1618; doc. at Palazzo Pitti in 1638

II-7
Peter Paul Rubens
*Ulysses on the Island of
the Phaeacians*
wood panel, inv. 1912
no. 9
1627
FS. AL (1737)
(see II-2)

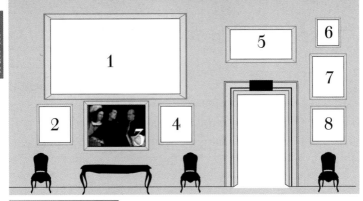

Wall III

III-1
Salvator Rosa
Seascape at Sunset
canvas, inv. 1912 no. 4
GC. M
(see I-5)

III-2
Titian
copy of the *Portrait
of Pope Julius II*
by Raphael
wood panel, inv. 1912 no. 79
1545
doc. at Palazzo Pitti in 1723
V. DR (1631)

III-3
Titian
The Concert
canvas, inv. 1912 no. 185
L. M (1654)

This portrait of three musicians was painted around 1510 when Titian was still working under his master Giorgione and it is one of the artist's most famous works from his juvenile period. It was bought at a high price by Cardinal Leopoldo de' Medici in 1654 through the agent Paolo del Sera as a work by Giorgione. It is notable for its intense realism as well as the naturalistic portrayal of the central musician's reaction when his companion, who places a hand on his shoulder, interrupts him.

III-4
Sebastiano del Piombo
*Portrait of Baccio
Valori*
slate, inv. 1912 no. 409
c. 1531
doc. in 1553
C I. M

III-5
Tintoretto
*Venus, Cupid and
Vulcan*
canvas, inv. 1912 no. 3
c. 1550–1555
C. M (1666)

III-6
Flemish school,
17th century
*Portrait of Pietro
Francavilla*
canvas, inv. 1890 no. 774
c. 1610
L. M

III-7
Salvator Rosa
Allegory of Falsehood
canvas, inv. 1912 no. 2
c. 1650–1660
GPF. M (1698)

III-8
Bartolomeo Passerotti
Portrait of a Man
canvas, inv. 1912 no. 138
c. 1570

II

Wall IV

IV-1
Justus Suttermans
Portrait of an Artist
canvas, inv. 1890 no. 781
doc. in 1797

IV-2
Justus Suttermans (?)
*Portrait of Vittoria
della Rovere as
St. Ursula*
canvas, inv. 1890 no. 5169
c. 1637
V. DR (1691)

IV-3
Justus Suttermans
Portrait of a Child
canvas, inv. 1890 no. 2404
c. 1631
V. DR (1691)

IV-4
Justus Suttermans
*Portrait of Alessandro
Farnese*
canvas, inv. 1890 no. 2203
1639–1640
V. DR (1692)

IV-5
Titian (?)
Ecce Homo
canvas, inv. 1912 no. 31
doc. in 1623–1624; doc. at
Palazzo Pitti in 1652
V. DR (1631)

IV-6
Guercino
St. Joseph
canvas, inv. 1912 no. 29
c. 1660
doc. at Palazzo Pitti in
1761

IV-7
Titian's studio
Adoration of the Child
canvas, inv. 1912 no. 483
V. DR (1631) ?

IV-8
Cigoli
*Vocation of Peter and
Andrew*
canvas, inv. 1912 no. 27
signed and dated 1607
doc. at Palazzo Pitti in
1628
C. L

IV-9
Giovanni Bilivert
St. Isidore the Farmer
canvas, inv. 1912 no. 25
c. 1612–1615
L. M (1675)

IV-10
Guido Reni
St. Joseph
canvas, inv. 1912 no. 24
c. 1639–1640
L. M (1675)

IV-11
Sienese school,
17th century (after
Francesco Vanni)
*Mystical Marriage of
St. Catherine of Siena*
canvas, inv. 1912 no. 32
post 1610
doc. in 1772

IV-12
Francesco Curradi
Narcissus at the Spring
canvas, inv. 1912 no. 10
signed and dated 1622
C. M.

IV-13
Rutilio Manetti
*Death of St. Mary
Magdalene*
canvas, inv. 1912 no. 23
c. 1618–1620

Green Room and the King's Bedroom

Artists

Collectors

Medici family

A. M - Antonio (1576–1621), son of Bianca Cappello, Grand Duchess from 1578

AML. M - Anna Maria Luisa Electress Palatine (1667–1743), daughter of Cosimo III and last in the family line

C. L - Cristina of Lorraine (1563–1637), consort of Ferdinando I and Grand Duchess from 1589

C. M - Cardinal Carlo (1595–1666), brother of Cosimo II and Cardinal from 1615

C I. M - Duke and Grand Duke Cosimo I (1519–1574), Duke from 1537 and Grand Duke from 1569

C II. M - Grand Duke Cosimo II (1590–1621), Grand Duke from 1609

C III. M - Grand Duke Cosimo III (1642–1723), Grand Duke from 1670

CL. M - Claudia (1604–1648), consort of Federico Ubaldo Della Rovere and mother of Vittoria della Rovere

DL. M - Don Lorenzo (1599–1648), brother of Cosimo II

F I. M - Cardinal and Grand Duke Ferdinando I (1549–1609), Cardinal from 1562 and Grand Duke from 1587

Fr I. M - Grand Duke Francesco I (1541–1587), Grand Duque from 1574

F II. M - Grand Duke Ferdinando II (1610–1670), Grand Duke from 1621

FM. M - Cardinal Francesco Maria (1660–1710), brother of Cosimo III and Cardinal from 1686

GC. M - Cardinal Giovan Carlo (1611–1663), brother of Ferdinando II and Cardinal from 1644

GG. M - Giovan Gastone (1671–1737), Grand Duke from 1623

GPF. M - Grand Prince Ferdinando (1663–1713), son of Cosimo III

L. M - Prince and Cardinal Leopoldo (1617–1675), brother of Ferdinando II and Cardinal from 1667

MM. A - Maria Magdalena of Austria (1589–1631), consort of Cosimo II and Grand Duchess from 1608

M. M - Mattias (1613–1667), brother of Ferdinando II

O. M - Ottaviano (1484–1546), belonged to a different branch of the family

VB. B - Violante Beatrice of Bavaria (1673–1731), consort of Grand Prince Ferdinando from 1689

V. DR - Vittoria della Rovere (1622–1694), consort of Ferdinando II and Grand Duchess from 1634

Hapsburg Lorraine family

F III. AL - Ferdinand III (1769–1824), Grand Duke from 1790

FS. AL - Francis Stephen (1708–1765), Grand Duke from 1737

L II. AL - Leopold II (1797–1870), Grand Duke from 1824 to 1859

PL. AL - Peter Leopold (1747–1792), Grand Duke from 1765 to 1790

Inventories

1588 - F I. M (1588):
Inventario di Villa Medici,
1588 (A.S.F. Guardaroba
Medicea 79)

1621 - A. M (1621):
*Inventario di oggetti
appartenenti all'eredità
di don Antonio de' Medici,*
1621

1631 - V. DR (1631):
*Conti della Serenissima
Granduchessa Vittoria,*
1631–1638 (A.S.F.
Guardaroba Medicea 955)

1649 - DL. M (1649): (A.S.F.
Guardaroba Medicea)
inventario del Serenissimo
Principe Don Lorenzo [de'
Medici]

1666 - C. M (1666):
*Inventario originale
dell'eredità del Cardinale
Decano,* 1666 (A.S.F.
Guardaroba Medicea 399)

1675 - L. M (1675):
*Inventario dei mobili e
masserizie dell'eredità del
Serenissimo e Reverendo
Signor Cardinal Leopoldo
de' Medici,* 1675-1676
(A.S.F. Guardaroba
Medicea 826)

1713 - GPF. M (1713):
*Inventario dei Mobili e
Masserizie della proprietà
del Ser. mo Principe
Ferdinando di Gloriosa
ricordanza, ritrovate doppo
la di lui morte nel suo
appartamento nel Palazzo
de' Pitti,* 1713 (A.S.F.
Guardaroba Medicea 1222)

1860 - Poggio Imperiale:
*Inventario degli Oggetti
di Belle Arti esistenti nella
Reale Villa del Poggio
Imperiale,* 1860

1890 - *Inventario Gallerie
Fiorentine,* 1890

1911 - OdA: *Inventario
Oggetti d'Arte di dotazione
della Corona nel Real
Palazzo Pitti,* 1911

1911- Petraia: *Inventario
Oggetti d'Arte della Real
Villa della Petraia,* 1911

1911 - Poggio a Caiano:
*Inventario Oggetti d'Arte
della Real Villa di Poggio a
Caiano,* 1911

1912 - *Inventario Galleria
Palatina,* 1912

1914 - Sculture: *Inventario
Sculture,* 1914

GDSU: *Inventario
Gabinetto Disegni e Stampe
degli Uffizi*